# SCHOLASTIC COLLECTIONS

Compiled by Brian Moses

# Stories From the Past

© 1994 Scholastic Ltd

3456789    6789012345

Published by Scholastic Ltd,
Villiers House,
Clarendon Avenue,
Leamington Spa,
Warwickshire CV32 5PR

**Compiler** Brian Moses
**Editors** Jane Wright and Christine Lee
**Assistant editors** Sophie Jowett and Kate Banham
**Series designer** Joy White
**Designer** Anna Oliwa
**Cover and illustrations** Peter Stevenson

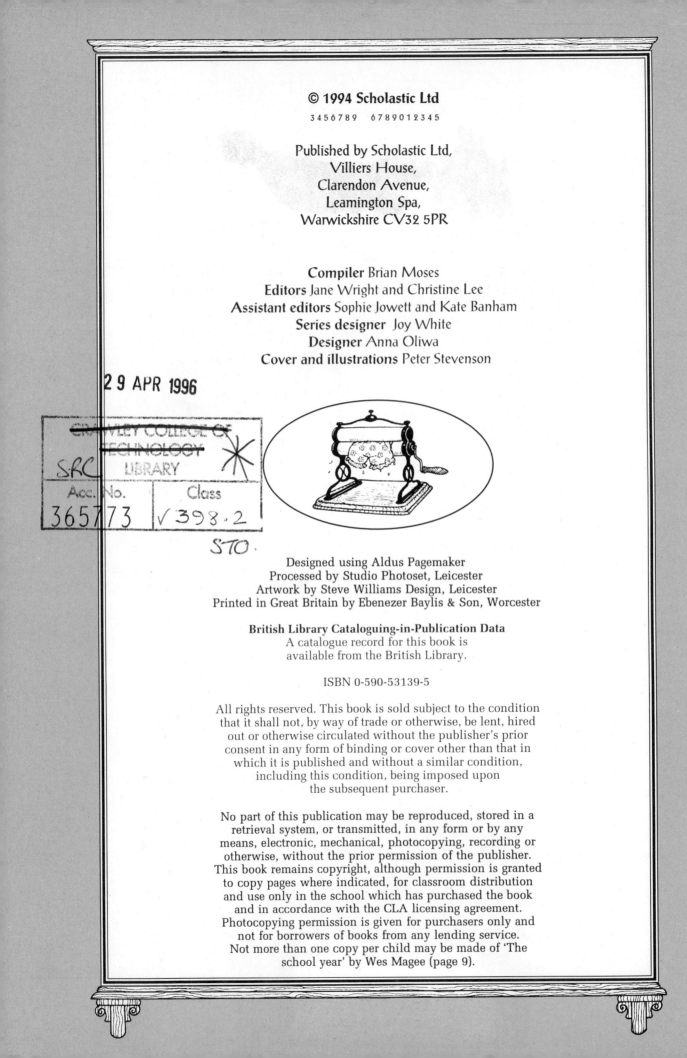

Designed using Aldus Pagemaker
Processed by Studio Photoset, Leicester
Artwork by Steve Williams Design, Leicester
Printed in Great Britain by Ebenezer Baylis & Son, Worcester

**British Library Cataloguing-in-Publication Data**
A catalogue record for this book is
available from the British Library.

ISBN 0-590-53139-5

# Contents

## INTRODUCTION

## CHANGES: PEOPLE, PLACES, TIMES

## INVADERS AND SETTLERS

## TUDORS

## VICTORIANS

## BRITAIN SINCE 1930

# GREEKS

# EXTENSION STUDIES

# INTRODUCTION

*Teachers should use stories, including extracts from myths and legends, where appropriate, as a major source of knowledge about the past for young pupils. They should be used together with other historical sources to enable pupils both to visualise, and acquire information about, the lives of people in the past.*

(*Final Report of the National Curriculum History Working Party*)

The stories featured in this volume of Collections cover a variety of genres – narrative, verse, diary extracts, letters, scripts, biographical sketches. Together, they represent a vast range of material to support different projects that may be linked to the various study units in the National Curriculum for history. Some of them can be read easily by the children themselves, and some will need to be read or retold by the teacher.

It is important that children understand the difference between factual accounts, some of which will be contemporary observation, and fiction that is based on fact. Indeed, one of the statements of attainment at Key Stage 1 is the ability to distinguish between real people from the past and fictional characters.

Stories are important in helping children to develop a sense of chronology. If they are asked to retell a story, children will be practising sequencing skills – what happened first of all, what followed from that and so on. Stories reveal, too, how people and places change over time and children can be questioned about the changes that take place, how they come about and what effects they have.

A story may act as a stimulus for further historical investigation. The poems and stories about grandparents in the Key Stage 1 section of this book will encourage children to talk about the past to their own grandparents, giving them a first-hand experience of oral history. This will, in turn, help them to focus on answers to questions such as 'Where did I come from?' 'What happened to my family before I was born?' and so on. With older children, reading about the past will encourage them to research background details in books, visit museums and handle artefacts.

Much of this material is photocopiable and may be used in various ways:

• Group presentations: children could share a piece of prose or a poem, list important facts or issues and present findings to the rest of the class.

• Cloze procedure: the teacher should hand out photocopied pages where certain information has been deleted. Children can use reference books to discover the missing information.

• Exploring different genres: a series of diary entries could be rewritten as, for example, a news report or a letter.

• Panel of experts: a small group could read a story or a poem and research it further. The rest of the class should draw up a list of twenty questions that can be put to the panel.

• Sequencing: children could rewrite the selection as a storyboard for a video shoot.

• Rewriting a story using speech bubbles. What did the characters *actually* say?

• Dramatising a story, either as a set script or as an improvisation. The story could be performed using puppets.

• Writing from a different viewpoint: one group writes about the discovery of the Wooden Horse of Troy from the Greek perspective, the other puts the Trojan point of view.

• Reading other versions of a story: do they differ? Why do they differ? The children should then decide whether there are statements which are factual and others which are points of view.

• Collecting artefacts that relate to the story: for young children, it is often the artefacts that set them thinking about who used them and how.

Through stories children learn to empathise. What was it like to end up poor, homeless and in an institution (*The workhouse),* sailing in Tudor times (*Setting sail with John Cabot 1497*) or to be caught out in the open when bombs started to fall (*Air raid on Guernsey*)? 'The children of change' by James Kirkup focuses on the ease with which children are able to take themselves into other worlds and to become whatever they wish to be. This ability can be channelled through questioning so that children are drawn to consider historical evidence.

# The children of change

The Universe is transformation: our life is what our thoughts make it.
(Marcus Aurelius: Meditations)

We are the children of change.
Whatever we think of, we can become –
a horse, a house, a bike, a mountain range,
a flower, a book, a toothbrush or a drum.

The way we walk, the way we jump and run
turns us into trains or scarecrows,
giraffes or octopuses, bouncing balls
or birds. The way we eat and sit and breathe

allows us to alter – we can be quite old,
like ancient warriors, or goddesses of Greece,
simply by taking thought; or transform ourselves
into the youngest things in all creation –

raindrops, grass, a new-discovered word, wild
strawberries, a baby elephant, a flame, a faun,
the first star of evening, a cloud shadow,
mysterious ripple on a lake, or breeze of dawn –

All these, and countless other things we can become
at will, and through imagination re-create ourselves
into something familiar or funny, rich and strange –
for we are the children, the children of change.

James Kirkup

# CHANGES: PEOPLE, PLACES, TIMES

## The school year

*September* starts a fresh school year,
new pupils feel a twinge of fear.
Our Harvest Festival's displayed;
our thanks to farmers duly made.

*October's* damp; the leaves fall down.
We make a book called 'Our Home Town'.
Big pictures pinned on wall and door;
there's thick mud on the cloakroom floor.

*November* brings us Bonfire Night
with blazing Guy and fireworks bright.
The Christmas plays – rehearsals start.
Who'll sing songs? Who'll speak a part?

*December's* cold; there's frost and snow
To 'Peter Pan' in town we go.
We decorate the school, have treats;
at parties there are prizes, sweets.

*January's* iced; pond frozen hard.
The snowmen freeze in our school yard,
but sliding and snowballing's banned.
This classroom's coldest in the land!

*February's* slushed with hail and sleet.
Make Valentines... for someone sweet.
Pancakes tossed and caught and eaten.
Snowdrops tell you winter's beaten.

*March* is wild; gales from the hills.
Our classroom bulbs... are daffodils!
A Pet Show's held... no dogs or cats.
For Easter we paint eggs, make hats.

*April's* fresh; spring's in the air,
slow buds unfurling everywhere.
Our topic title – 'Beast and Bird'.
The year's first cuckoo can be heard.

*May* comes cool, but trees still drip.
We leave for our field-study trip
and visit castles, climb steep hills
and get soaked through and all catch chills.

*June's* so warm; the summer's here.
Our Sports Day banners wave; we cheer.
That loud crack is the starter's gun.
Our parents watch us jump and run.

*July!* Phew, hot! The days are long.
We give a concert... dance and song.
For Open Night our work's on show.
At Leavers' Disco faces glow.

*August*... time for holidays,
whole weeks to simply lounge and laze.
On beach, in caravan, at home
you're free to come and go, to roam.

The school year's gone, our teachers smile.
Forget the book work... for a while.
But soon September's here, and then
we all troop back to school again.

Wes Magee

# Changing Times

Many things are changing
Today in London Town
New buildings going up
Old ones coming down
Just like London people
Houses too grow old
And can no longer do their job
To keep out damp and cold
Many are old fashioned
And were built long ago
For people in a different age
Who didn't hurry so
People's ways are changing
Like the things we use
Telephones for speaking
Television news
Just try to imagine
How things used to be
Different songs to listen to
Different things to see
Everyone used horses
Or else their own two feet
Everything moved slowly
Like the policeman on his beat
No motor cars to take them
Quickly on their way
No discos or videos
Like there are today
No package holidays
And no aeroplanes
No electric railways
And only puffer trains
People used to manage
It didn't matter how
But when you come to think of it
Aren't you glad it's NOW.

Eric Slayter

# The blacksmith

When the darkness falls and the air grows chill
And the lights go out in the village store,
Then a crowd of folk always makes its way
To the flickering glow from the blacksmith's door

To see Mr Smutts and his red-faced twins
Beat the white-hot iron till the sparks fly high,
As they shape a shoe for the farmer's horse,
Or they mend a gate for the pigman's sty,

Or they fix a blade on a broken skate,
Or they make a bell for a goat or cow.
And they sing and sweat in the smoke and flames,
And the audience claps as they take their bow.

From Our Village by John Yeoman

# Mr Mandolini and his dancing bear

The hurdy gurdy's playing,
All the people run and stare,
For it's Mr Mandolini
And his dancing bear.

You've seen them on the village green,
You've seen them at the fair –
Old Mr Mandolini
And his dancing bear.

The grown-ups rock with laughter
But the children are aware
That there's really nothing sadder
Than a dancing bear.

From Our Village by John Yeoman

# The two Annas

Great-grandma Anna always had to get up very early.
Every day she and her brother walked nearly two miles to school.
The narrow country road used to get flooded after heavy rain.

It is only a short walk from home to the school bus.
If it is raining Mum takes me to the bus-stop in the car.
My friends from the new housing estate join the bus at the next stop.

In those days the school was not much bigger than an ordinary house.
It had only one classroom and one teacher.
The teacher lived in the rooms above the schoolroom.

The children sat at wooden desks with hinged lids.
Each desk had a little inkwell which they dipped their pens into.
On cold mornings the teacher lit the wood-burning stove.

The town is much bigger today, so there are more schoolchildren.
Several new classrooms have been added to the old building.
Most of our teachers are women.

I sit near the window, just where my great-grandma used to be.
The classrooms look much more cheerful than in the olden days.
Today Miss Morgan is teaching us about sets.

Every day Great-grandma Anna had lots of chores to do.
In autumn she picked apples from the orchard.
Each day she fed the rabbits and carried milk home from the dairy.

After school there was more work for Great-grandma to do.
She fed the hens and collected their eggs.
Poor Great-grandma didn't have much time for playing.

Today there are not nearly so many jobs to be done.
After I have finished my homework I like to go roller-skating.
Or sometimes I play ball, or go for a cycle ride.

In the evening I get out my family of dolls.
Last year Mum and Dad gave me their old television, and
I am allowed to watch a programme before bedtime.

From Anna Then and Anna Now by Josette Blanco and Claude d'Ham

# Photographs

Who's that figure standing there,
slim at the waist, shoulder length hair?
That's your dad twenty years ago,
wouldn't think so now though.

Who's that young girl skipping high,
caught against a sunny sky?
That's your mum some years ago,
looks a bit different now though.

Who's that tall and lanky lad,
looks a little bit like dad?
That's his brother, Uncle Joe,
wouldn't know him now though.

Who's that lady by the swing,
practising her curtseying?
That's Auntie many years ago,
she doesn't dance much now though.

Who's that tiny wrinkled baby,
mouth wide open, bawling loudly?
Oh come on now, surely you know,
you're still a noisy so and so!

Brian Moses

# Looking back

Gas lamps were first used in the early 19th century. To begin with they flickered badly and didn't give out much light. Later on they were fitted with mantles. A mantle was a small piece of stiffened cotton net which had been coated with chemicals which, when hot, glowed with a strong white light. In those houses which had a gas supply, people began to use gas cookers.
Before World War II most people had a coal fire in their living room.

We had a black iron gas cooker with three burners. The cooker didn't belong to you, it belonged to the gas company. You had to put pennies in the meter. We kept a supply of pennies in case the gas ran out.

The coal was kept in a coal cellar. It was delivered by a coalman who emptied the sacks into the cellar through a hole in the pavement. When mother was out, we used to break into the house by lifting up the cast iron plate and sliding down on to the heap of coals below. Then we'd go up the cellar steps, down the passage and open the front door.

Life for me is very different to my mother's. I now have electricity – I can just press a switch on the wall and I have instant light. No more buying inverted mantles and matches.

My bathroom is now a cosy room with a toilet. No more carrying buckets of water. I go to the bath, turn on the taps and have instant hot water. No more hotting up buckets of water on the fire anymore. For heating I walk across the room, turn a knob on the radiator and instantly I have a warm flat. No more lighting a fire with paper, sticks and coal and picking up the ashes every morning.

*From A Century of Change: 20th Century Homes by John Foster*

# Grandad's washday

One morning, when Sally had been spending the night with Granny and Grandad, she went out to look at her garden. The seeds were coming up and she was so excited that she ran to tell Grandad. It had rained in the night and the ground was slippery. Poor Sally slipped and fell. When Grandad helped her up she was covered in mud.

'Oh, what a messy Sally!' said Grandad. 'Let's try and clean you up before your Gran comes back from the shops. Did you bring any other clothes?'

Sally nodded, still crying.

'Well, you'd better wash your hands and face and change into those clothes while I put these in the washing machine. No, don't drip mud all the way upstairs. Leave your trainers and muddy clothes here.'

When Sally came down in her clean sweater and jeans the muddy ones were already going round in the washing machine and Grandad had made himself a cup of coffee. He offered Sally the biscuit tin.

'Reminds me of when I dared your Great Auntie Beryl to jump across our garden pond. She fell in and came out covered in mud and green slime. We both got sent to bed.'

'Did her things go in the washing machine?' asked Sally.

'Oh, no! Some people had very simple washing machines in those days, but we didn't. All our washing had to be done by hand. That's why your

Great-gran was so cross. Washing was hard work in those days.'

'Why was it hard work?' asked Sally.

'Well, on wash day my Mum, your Great-gran, got up very early and lit a fire to heat the water. We didn't hang about if we knew what was good for us. We had our breakfast and went to school. Washing took all day – all she had to help her was a board to rub things against and a stick to push the clothes around with. And there was the mangle, of course.'

'What's a mangle?' asked Sally.

Grandad scratched his head. 'It's hard to explain. Like two rolling pins, one on top of the other. You pushed the clothes through and turned the handle and they squeezed the water out of the clothes. No tumble-driers in those days. And you had to be very careful not to get your fingers caught in the mangle.'

When Gran came in she was very surprised to see Sally in different clothes.

'I can't leave you two for a few minutes without you getting into mischief, can I?' said Gran.

'Grandad's been telling me about washing day when he was little,' said Sally.

'Did he tell you it was always the same dinner on wash day? Cold meat from the Sunday roast and perhaps bubble and squeak if we were lucky. Mums were too busy to cook very much. What's the matter, dear? You look puzzled.'

'Why did you have bubbles for dinner?'

It was Gran's turn to look puzzled. Then she laughed.

'Bubble and squeak! That's mashed potato left over from Sunday lunch fried up with leftover greens.'

Sally wrinkled her nose. 'It sounds horrible!'

'Your Grandad thinks it's delicious. He grumbles because I won't cook it very often.'

'Why won't you?' asked Sally.

'Because salad is better for him. And if you're going into the garden again, Miss, put your apron on.'

Five minutes later Sally was back in the kitchen.

'It's a good job you've got a washing machine, Gran.'

'With grubby little girls like you around, it certainly is!'

'Not just me, Gran. Grandad's tripped over a stone and he's sitting in the pond!'

Marjorie Williams

# Grandad's clothes

'What did you wear
when you were my age, Grandpa?'
I asked.
'Did you wear T-shirts?
Did you wear jeans and trainers?'

Grandpa smiled
and got out his photo album.
He showed me a picture
of a small boy
in a white cotton shirt,
short trousers and long socks.

'That's what I wore
all the year round,'
he said.
'Only grown-ups wore long trousers.'

'Didn't your knees get cold?'
I asked.

'Of course, they did,'
he said.
'We just had to put up with it.
Nowadays, grown-ups have got more sense.'

John Foster

# Grandma's doll

Grandma's doll has a blue cotton
dress
And a white lace bonnet.

Her body is stuffed with straw
And feels stiff and hard.

Her head is made of china
And there are tiny cracks
All over her face.

'They look like wrinkles,'
I said.

'That's because she's old,'
Laughed Grandma.
'Like me.'

John Foster

# The corner shop

Scotch hands in the butter
Pat. Pat. Pat.
My dad served his customers
Just like that.

Rolls of bacon in the slicer
Whizz. Zin. Zin.
See the bacon slices
Thick. Thin. Thin.

Corona in big bottles
Pop. Pop. Pop.
And thruppence for the empties
In our grocer's shop.

Now food comes in packets
Sliding down conveyor belts.
Or it comes out of a freezer –
Hurry home before it melts.

The supermarket's bigger
A food-palace... All the same,
The lady on the check-out
Doesn't know your name.

Jan Dean

# Shopping lists

### 1. A Victorian labourer's wife:

Seven pints of porter,
five loaves of bread.
Put them on the shopping list
to keep the family fed.

Forty pounds of taters,
five pounds of meat.
How can people live and work
unless there's food to eat?

A pound of sugar, and butter, too,
three ounces of tea,
will have to get us through the week,
husband, children, me.

That's the lot, my darlings,
a week's money buys.
Anything you add to that
is wishes, dreams and lies.

### 2. A modern family:

Pizza and fish fingers,
cans of baked beans.
Lots of tins of fizzy,
that's what shopping means.

Drop them in the trolley,
take them to the till.
Pack them up and drive them home,
sit and eat your fill.

Sausages and bacon,
custard, yoghurts, eggs.
Biscuits, crisps, bananas,
packs of chicken legs.

Lettuce and tomatoes,
oranges and pears.
Tiny chocolate biscuits
shaped like teddy bears.

Our shopping trolley's full of things
to make you lick your lips.
'Can we have some sweets, Mum?
And don't forget the chips!'

Tony Mitton

# The magical machine

This poem is based on a genuine letter, written by a
Victorian woman to a friend and describing her first train journey.
The railways had only just been built.

I cannot say how strange it seemed
to journey in this way.
We sped so fast across the land
it took my breath away.

I stood up with my bonnet off
and drank the rushing air.
It seemed to me we flew along
without the lightest care.

I feel I've flown to fairyland
for I am one who's been
along the Swansea Railway Line
in the Magical Machine.

# The train to work

A child living now describes how her mother takes a
train to work every day.

My Mummy has to catch the train
that leaves at half-past eight.
She always has to rush a bit
because she can't be late.

The train is full of people
who chat, or read the news.
They're going off to do their jobs,
and that's the train they use.

My Mummy always goes to work
riding on this train.
And then, just after tea-time,
she comes back home again.

Tony Mitton

# Peter and Kate on the move

For weeks Peter and Kate had been getting ready for the Move. The family was moving to a new house some distance away and everyone was excited. Even Spot the dog knew something was going to happen and followed Dad everywhere.

Peter's and Kate's father had given them a big box so that they could pack their toys and treasures themselves. So, after a lot of argument, they chose their favourite books, *Peter Rabbit* and *The Wind in the Willows* (they both liked Toad best), Lego, a 'Space attack' game, a football, Kate's 'Barbie' doll with all its sets of clothes and Peter's Dinky cars.

'I shall take my carpentry tools so that I can help Dad with the jobs in the new house,' said Peter busily.

'I can help Dad too,' said Kate. 'I like banging things with a hammer!'

When he thought nobody was looking, Peter slipped in an old felt monkey, Jacko, that he had had since he was a little boy. 'You're not going to take that old thing, are you?' protested his mother. 'Yes, I am!' said Peter. 'I couldn't just leave Jacko here, Mummy.' He tucked his old friend away in a corner of the box where no one was likely to find him and throw him away.

The trouble was that as soon as the box was packed, Peter or Kate would be sure to want something out of it – a favourite doll or a special car – so the box was always in a state of confusion. At last, when the move was only two days away, Dad said, 'Now, that's enough! I'm going to tie up your box and you mustn't open it until we are safely in the new house.'

Now the exciting day of the move had come.

'Where are you going?' asked Peter's friend, Joe, from next door.

'I don't quite know – a long way – and it's a *new* house, new bricks, a new front door and...'

'Are you taking your swing?'

'No – Dad says he'll make me a new one.'

'Good! Then I'll swing on it when you've gone.'

'All right – but no one else can.'

'Goodbye. I may as well have a swing *now*,' said Joe and he disappeared into Peter's garden.

'Peter!' called his mother. 'The van's here.'

Sure enough, there it was. It looked as big as a house, thought Peter, but after all everything inside the house had to be put into it. It needed to be big!

He watched as the two removers' men carried the chairs and the tables and the big wardrobe and lots of other things and loaded them into the van. The men seemed to do a lot of shouting to each other. 'This way, Jim...' 'Mind your corners...!' 'Slowly does it...' 'Told you it wouldn't go, Fred. Look what you done!'

Peter thought Fred was a very funny man! He put an easy chair over his head, carried a small chair in one hand and frying pan in the other and hung a picture round his neck. All the time he sang and whistled. Moving was fun, Peter decided.

He ran upstairs to look at his bedroom again. To his dismay Jim and

Fred were knocking his bed into pieces. 'Hi!' he said indignantly, 'You're breaking up my bed!'

'Keep your hair on, young 'un,' said Jim. 'We'll put it together again when we get to the other end. If not, the floor's nice and comfortable.'

Peter was not at all sure about that.

At last the house was empty. The furniture was in the van, the carpets taken up, the curtains down. Peter's mother ran out with a last box of food and kitchen things and Daddy put in the box of plants he had grown in the greenhouse.

'Have you put in my potatoes?' asked Peter anxiously. His father had planted potatoes in the spring and Peter had planted some too.

'Sorry, Peter,' said his father. 'The potatoes aren't big enough to dig up yet and, anyway, they belong to the man who has bought our house.'

Someone else eating *his* potatoes – pounds and pounds of them! Peter didn't think that was at all fair. 'But, Dad...' he began.

'Let's go round the house and make sure nothing has been forgotten,' suggested his father hastily.

They looked into every room. It was strange to see them so empty and to hear their footsteps on the bare boards. There were light patches on the wallpaper where the pictures had hung. The house didn't feel like home anymore.

'Has anyone seen Cuddles?' asked Peter's Mum. 'I can't find her anywhere and I want to put her safely into the cat basket.'

Peter and Kate dashed about everywhere in the house, but there was nowhere to hide there now. Joe was still swinging in the garden but he said he hadn't seen Cuddles. Kate began to cry, 'Cuddles is lost – I don't want to leave Cuddles behind!'

'Would you by any chance be looking for a black cat with whiskers?' asked Fred, who had been looking round the van to make sure everything was secure. 'There's one asleep on the settee here.' And there was Cuddles curled up in her usual place on the settee.

'Best leave her there,' said Peter's Dad, 'but mind she doesn't get out at the other end until we're there.'

Fred and Jim clanged the big door of the van shut and moved off slowly. 'See yer!' they shouted.

Now it was the family's turn to pack themselves into their car. Peter and Kate climbed into the back seat – Spot had jumped in already for he loved car rides and he was afraid of being left behind. Mummy pushed in a lot of oddments round the children, Daddy filled the boot with others.

'We're off!' shouted Peter and Kate. 'Goodbye, house!'

At first they looked out of the car window but it had been an exciting day and they were tired. They fell asleep and Spot slept too, his nose on

Peter's foot.

When they woke they were nearly at the end of their journey. They looked out eagerly and Spot put his head out of the window, his ears flapping in the breeze.

'The first one who sees a school, *shout*!' said their father. 'Our house is in the next road to the school, on the left.'

'SCHOOL!' shouted Kate, and Dad turned into a rough road. There at the end was a new-looking house with green fields beyond. And there was the furniture van parked outside and Jim and Fred were sitting on the tailboard smoking.

'Ready when you are, mate,' said Jim. Soon they were unloading the van and carrying everything into the new house. Kate ran inside with the sleepy Cuddles in her arms. Before long, the new house was full of furniture and the van was empty. After a last cup of tea, Jim and Fred drove away.

Peter and Kate rushed into the house. 'Which is my room?' Peter asked eagerly.

'I want to see *my* room,' demanded Kate.

'The big bedroom at the front is for Daddy and me,' said their mother. 'The middle-sized room at the back is Peter's because he is the oldest and the little room is Kate's because she likes to be cosy.'

They ran upstairs. Peter was anxious about his bed – would Jim and Fred have mended it properly? Yes they had and it looked as good as new. And there was their special box at the foot of the bed. The window looked out over the garden and the fields. It was a super room!

'Look at my room!' said Kate. It too had a window looking out over the garden. 'I *like* my room,' said Kate contentedly.
'I shall put my dolls' house just here...'

'I'll make you some shelves with my carpentry set,' offered Peter kindly.

'I'll hammer the nails in,' said Kate.

'One quick look at the garden, children,' called their mother, 'then tea and bed. We're all tired.'

Kate was almost asleep and didn't want to go out, so Peter ran into the garden by himself, Spot barking at his heels with excitement – *he* wanted to find out what the new garden *smelt* like! The garden was big enough for Peter to play with his football and there weren't any flowerbeds to get in the way – not yet anyway. There were some thick bushes at the end, just right for playing Indians and hiding. Peter climbed the fence and looked out across the fields. What a long way he could see! There was a wood in the distance, it would be fun to explore that. He and Kate and Spot could have lots of fun together.

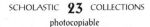

How hungry he was! He ran indoors for tea.

Later, as he snuggled down in his own bed with Jacko for company, he thought about his new home. It felt a bit strange but Mum and Dad were there and Kate and Spot and Cuddles, so everything would be all right. 'Tomorrow, Jacko,' he said sleepily, 'we'll explore and have adventures and...'

Peter and Kate were asleep in their new home.

From High Days and Holidays by Eileen Colwell

# The castle

I love the castle
On the hill;
When I'm there
Time stands still.

I walk around
The ruined walls,
Then wait inside
The ancient hall.

It has no roof,
But soon I hear
Something from
Across the years.

Knights and ladies,
Barking dogs,
Jesters joking,
Crackling logs.

Neighing horses,
Clash of steel,
Battle raging;
It's so *real*.

When I'm there
I might believe...
But no, it can't be.
Time to leave.

Tony Bradman

# My Mammy sen' for me

When Elizabeth's mother was offered work in England, she left her daughter with
Granny in Dominica, saying that she would send for her when she was settled.
When the time comes for Elizabeth to leave her Granny she doesn't want to leave
the people and places that she knows. On the flight to England she is very worried
about what she will find there.

When Elizabeth came to England she was so small she could hardly reach
Aunt Si Si's hand as she marched her up the steps of the aeroplane.
Elizabeth had never seen a train before, never mind the strange metal bird
she was boarding with this lady she hardly knew. Her gran had told her to
be good, and to sit quiet, and not to ask too many questions, so she had
pursed her lips together to lock the words in just in case a word wanted to
pop out.

'Humph,' she sighed.

Everybody else had been crying and touching her face like they would
never see her again. Her gran had turned away and pretended the sun was
in her eyes but Elizabeth knew she was crying.

'Send me some letter an' picture of you in Inglan,' her gran had said,
hugging Elizabeth ever so tightly. 'And don't forget us when you over
there.'

Forget? thought Elizabeth, careful not to let the word slip out. She
wiped some dirt from her new red and white cotton dress her gran had
made especially for the trip. Goodness knew how the dirt had got there.

'Forget...' she said to herself. How on earth could she forget her gran.
When Elizabeth sat down on the aeroplane she asked Aunt Si Si if she
could swap seats.

'I want to look out de window and wave at de birds.'

Aunt Si Si had a funny face, that always looked surprised. Her whole
face was made up of circles. Her eyes were two small circles and she had
dark oval spots for a nose and a hole like a fish's for a mouth. Even her
spectacles were round and she wore a round cane hat with a big round brim.

'You don't going see birds Elizabet' we going fly too high for dat.'

Elizabeth sulked. Instead she looked out of another window across the
aisle. She could see her gran and the others leaving, and for the first time
she felt alone. The little aeroplane was full of people, about sixteen in all,
but everybody was busy with something. Fastening their seatbelts, getting
comfortable in their seats or just generally being excited. Elizabeth
though, had a heavy feeling in her stomach; like she had swallowed a big
stone. She could feel her eyes pricking ready to cry, and her aunt (who
wasn't really her aunt but a friend of her gran's going to England on
holiday, who she had been told to call Aunt Si Si) didn't even notice the
tears.

'I feeling sick,' Elizabeth said, pulling at Aunt Si Si's sleeve.

'My belly rolling. Why de plane shaking so?'

Aunt Si Si put her hand on Elizabeth's stomach and rubbed it for her.
'Here's a sweety,' she said, reaching in her pocket and handing it to
Elizabeth.

'My ears making vroom vroom and pop-pop,' Elizabeth said, mimicking the sound of the plane's engine. Her aunt told her to put her fingers in her ears which Elizabeth did, and she leaned over Aunt Si Si's knee and watched the clouds. Elizabeth was tired. Tired. Excited. Sad. Afraid. Supposing she didn't like England? Supposing she didn't make any friends? Did England have yards in which she could play skipping and hide and seek? And what about the sea? Would she be able to swim every day like she did in Dominica? And would it be cold... too cold? She'd heard stories about England and she wanted so much to be back with her friends Adria and Avaline in the school yard. She had cried when she had said goodbye to them. Miss George, her teacher, had announced to the whole class that Elizabeth would be leaving and Elizabeth had explained why.

'My mammy sen' for me. Granny say' she was only taking care of me for a little time, 'til Mammy have money to pay my passage.'

'Chil', fix your face,' Aunt Si Si said, pinching Elizabeth's cheeks and forcing her to smile. 'You can't reach Inglan wid such a miserable face.'

'I want to go back home,' Elizabeth said, unhappily.

'Wha' you mean you want to go back home? You' Mammy sen' for you to come and meet her and everybody waiting.'

'Everybody who?' asked Elizabeth.

'Your mammy, your cousins Reuben and Nicko, Aunty Lilian, Uncle Isaac, Aunty May May... all a dem.'

'Is there a garden,' Elizabeth asked, 'wid Fig and Banana, Coconut, Grapefruit, Hot Pepper...?'

'Is food you thinking about?' Aunt Si Si laughed. 'Well is one thing I am sure about Elizabet' you not going starve. Your Mammy' cupboard will be full.'

Elizabeth smiled. From the garden to the cupboard, she thought, and she fell asleep content. She was still half asleep when she got off the small aeroplane in Antigua and on to the big aeroplane which would take them to England.

From Mammy, Sugar Falling Down by Trish Cooke

# Spaceman James

Gran had bought James a space suit for his birthday. James liked it so much he insisted on wearing it every day. Mum wouldn't let him go to school in it but he put it on as soon as he got home. He even tried to have tea with the helmet on until Mum said, 'No, James!' in her don't-be-silly voice.

'I think you look stupid,' said Lisa.

James stuck out his tongue.

'Mind your own business. Girls don't know anything about space.'

'Yes, they do!' said Lisa.

'No, they don't!' said James.

'Do!'

'Don't!'

'Quiet!' said Dad. 'I can't hear the news.'

Lisa thought that the news was a very boring programme. She was about to go into the garden when Dad said, 'Quick, children. Look! There's a real spaceman!'

They looked at the screen and saw an ordinary man, looking like someone's Grandad.

'He's not a spaceman!' said James. 'Where's his helmet?'

'He used to be a spaceman.'

'What's his name, Dad? How do you know he was a spaceman?' asked Lisa.

'His name was John Glenn and he was once very famous. He orbited the earth in his spaceship. It often happens now but then it was very exciting.'

'What does "orbited" mean?' asked Lisa.

'He went round the earth,' said Dad.

'I'm orbiting the table!' said James, running round it.

'Yes, but how do you know?' persisted Lisa.

'The papers and the radio and television were full of it,' said Dad. 'I remember our headteacher announcing it in assembly that Major Glenn was orbiting the earth and we all cheered. He was the first American to orbit the earth. A Soviet spaceman, Yuri Gagarin, had orbited the earth one year earlier. Until then space flights had only been in adventure stories. Now it was real.'

'How old were you, Dad?' asked James.

'Oh, nine or ten.' Dad got up and fetched the big encyclopaedia. After turning the pages for some time he said, 'Here it is. Look. It says that Major John Glenn orbited the earth three times in his spacecraft, *Friendship Seven*, on 20 February, 1962.

The children looked. There was a photograph of a smiling young man in a space helmet.

'Tell you what,' said Dad. 'One Saturday we can go to the Science Museum. There are lots of interesting things to see there – all about spacemen – and women!'

'Told you so!' said Lisa.

James put on his helmet again. 'I'm going to orbit the garden!' he shouted.

'Oh, no, you're not!' Mum had come in. 'That isn't moon dust on you, it's real dirt. Goodnight, Spaceman James!'

Marjorie Williams

# Mum Dad and Me

My parents grew among palmtrees,
in sunshine strong and clear.
I grow in weather that's pale,
misty, watery or plain cold,
around back streets of London.

Dad swam in warm sea, at my age.
I swim in a roofed pool.
Mum – she still doesn't swim.

Mum went to an open village market
at my age. I go to a covered
arcade one with her now.
Dad works most Saturdays.

At my age Dad played
cricket with friends.
Mum helped her mum, or talked
shouting halfway up a hill.
Now I read or talk on the phone.

With her friends Mum's mum washed
clothes on a river-stone. Now
washing-machine washes our clothes.
We save time to eat to TV,
never speaking.

My dad longed for a freedom in Jamaica.
I want a greater freedom.
Mum prays for us, always.

Mum goes to church
some evenings and Sundays.
I go to the library.
Dad goes for his darts at the local.

Mum walked everywhere, at my age.
Dad rode a donkey.
Now I take a bus
or catch the underground train.

James Berry

# Florence Nightingale and Mary Seacole

Over a hundred years ago British soldiers were sent to fight a war in a part of Russia, called the Crimea. It was a long way from home and, as there were no aeroplanes in those days, things the soldiers needed took a long time to arrive from London. They were even short of food, boots and other clothes some of the time. If they were wounded in battle or caught a disease called cholera, there were not enough bandages or medicine to make them better. There were no proper hospitals, no doctors or nurses until two famous women travelled to Russia to help look after the soldiers.

Mary Seacole came from Kingston, Jamaica. Her father was an army officer and her mother looked after sick soldiers in her own home. Mary learnt about cholera there and how to mix medicines which would help the soldiers get better. When she heard about the epidemic in the Crimean War, she travelled to London and asked to be sent out as a nurse. The War Office turned her down, but she still thought she could help, so she decided to travel on her own and see what she could do when she got there. She paid her own fare and when she arrived, set up a canteen, which she called The British Hotel, two miles from the battlefield. Every day she filled her basket with food, drink and medicine which she took to the soldiers in the camp.

Florence Nightingale also wanted to go to the Crimea as a nurse. She came from a rich Hampshire family who were shocked when she told them she wanted to run a hospital. In those days women like Florence were expected to stay at home all day and not work for a living. Her family certainly didn't think nursing was a respectable thing to do. But, like Mary Seacole, Florence thought she could help, and made up her mind to go to the Crimea. After making a lot of fuss, she persuaded someone in the government to pay for herself and a small group of nurses to go and open a proper hospital. When they arrived, they found everything in a terrible condition. There were not enough beds, no bandages, medicine or even soap. It was hard to keep the place clean and to stop the cholera from spreading. She found that more soldiers were dying from disease than from their battle wounds. Florence Nightingale wrote angry letters back home to her friend in the government, complaining about the lack of supplies. Meanwhile she set to work to get the hospital working as well as she could. Every night she went round to talk to the soldiers lying in bed. She carried an oil lamp with her and held it up to see who they were. They didn't know her name, but called her the lady with the lamp.

One person who saw both Mary Seacole and Florence Nightingale at work was a newspaper reporter called William Russell. He worked for the *Times* in London and sent back reports about the two women. When they got back to England they were both national heroines.

Mary Seacole soon became ill herself. First she wrote a book about her life called *The Wonderful Adventures of Mary Seacole in Many Lands*. The soldiers collected money for a Seacole Fund that would support her in her old age. Mary was very grateful because it meant she could go back to her home in Jamaica for the last time.

Florence Nightingale founded the first training school for nurses at St Thomas' Hospital in London. She also wrote a book about how hospitals should be designed and organised.

Sallie Purkis

# The Olympic Games

Every four years, sportsmen and women from all over the world meet each other at the modern Olympic Games. The meeting is held in a different city each time. When the city is chosen, the people begin to prepare. First they build a big stadium and a swimming pool, then an Olympic village where the athletes will live while the Games are on. The opening ceremony is very exciting. All round the stadium fly flags from every country, bands play, there are displays of dancing and finally there is a big procession, when all the athletes march round the stadium. But the highlight is when a runner appears carrying a flaming torch. The flame has been carried all the way from Olympia in Greece, because that is where the Ancient Greeks held their Olympic Games two thousand seven hundred years ago.

When the flame appears everyone in the stadium gives a big cheer and flocks of white doves are released. Doves are a symbol of peace. During the Games the countries of the world come to take part in peaceful sports, not to fight against each other in a war.

Some of the events held in the modern Olympic Games are the same as in the ancient Games. The Greeks had running races, relay races, wrestling and boxing matches. They also had a special prize for the Pentathlon. To win this an athlete had to take part in five events, running, jumping, wrestling, discus and javelin throwing. All these events happen in the modern Games too.

But lots of things today are different. We don't have chariot races with chariots drawn by teams of horses. In the ancient Games the chariots had to do twelve laps of the stadium. Sometimes forty or more chariots took part and they often collided with each other. Our athletes don't have special events where they have to wear heavy armour either. In the ancient Games at Olympia only men could take part; in the modern Games men and women join in. The prizes are also different, although the idea behind them is the same. There are no money prizes. In Ancient Greece, every winner was given a circle of olive leaves to wear on his head. In the modern Games the winners are given gold, silver or bronze medals to wear.

If you wanted to watch the Games in Ancient Greece, you had to travel there in person. Today, we can watch the Games at home on television. So every four years, people who like watching sport enjoy themselves almost as much as the athletes who take part.

Sallie Purkis

# INVADERS

# First invasion of Britain by Julius Caesar (55 BC)

When Julius Caesar sailed across the English Channel with about 80 warships, the
fleet were faced with high cliffs at Dover from which the enemy forces could hurl
down weapons and missiles onto the Roman soldiers if they tried to land. Caesar
then moved along the coast until he found a place where the land sloped to the sea,
but was unable to get his ships close enough to the shore. His soldiers then faced
three difficulties – jumping from the ships while weighed down by their armour,
keeping upright in the water and fighting enemy forces who were on familiar
ground. In spite of these problems, Caesar's soldiers managed to drive off the enemy.
This extract is from the memoirs of Julius Caesar, the earliest eye-witness
account of Britain and its native people.

The natives had sent forward their cavalry and a number of the chariots
which they are accustomed to use in warfare; the rest of their troops
followed close behind and were ready to oppose the landing. The Romans
were faced with very grave difficulties. The size of the ships made it
impossible to run them aground except in fairly deep water; and the
soldiers, unfamiliar with the ground with their hands full, and weighed
down by the heavy burden of their arms, had at the same time to jump
down from the ships, get a footing in the waves, and fight the enemy,

who, standing on dry land or advancing only a short way into the water, fought with all their limbs unencumbered and on perfectly familiar ground, boldly hurling javelins and galloping their horses, which were trained to this kind of work. These perils frightened our soldiers, who were quite unaccustomed to battles of this kind, with the result that they did not show the same alacrity and enthusiasm as they usually did in battles on dry land.

Seeing this, Caesar ordered the warships – which were swifter and easier to handle than the transports, and likely to impress the natives more by their unfamiliar appearance – to be removed a short distance from the others, and then to be rowed hard and run ashore on the enemy's right flank, from which position slings, bows, and artillery could be used by men on deck to drive them back. This manoeuvre was highly successful. Scared by the strange shape of the warships, the motion of the oars, and the unfamiliar machines, the natives halted and then retreated a little. But as the Romans still hesitated, chiefly on account of the depth of the water, the man who carried the eagle of the 10th legion, after praying to the gods that his action might bring good luck to the legion, cried in a loud voice: 'Jump down, comrades, unless you want to surrender our eagle to the enemy; I, at any rate, mean to do my duty to my country and my general.' With these words he leapt out of the ship and advanced towards the enemy with the eagle in his hands. At this the soldiers, exhorting each other not to submit to such a disgrace, jumped with one accord from the ship, and the men from the next ships, when they saw them, followed them and advanced against the enemy. Both sides fought hard. But as the Romans could not keep their ranks or get a firm foothold or follow their proper standards, and men from different ships fell in under the first standard they came across, great confusion resulted. The enemy knew all the shallows, and when they saw from the beach small parties of soldiers disembarking one by one, they galloped up and attacked them at a disadvantage, surrounding, them with superior numbers, while others would throw javelins at the right flank of a whole group. Caesar therefore ordered the warships' boats and the scouting-vessels to be loaded with troops, so that he could send help to any point where he saw the men in difficulties. As soon as the soldiers had got a footing on the beach and had waited for all their comrades to join them, they charged the enemy and put them to flight, but could not pursue very far, because the cavalry had not been able to hold their course and make the island. This was the one thing that prevented Caesar from achieving his usual success.

**Footnotes:**
*Cavalry* – *troops who fight on horseback.*
*Warships* – *ships carrying soldiers.*
*Transports* – *ships carrying men, horses and military equipment.*
*Legion* – *a group of soldiers that form part of an army. The Roman army was divided into legions of about 5000 men.*
*Standard* – *each legion had its own standard called an eagle. This was carried by a standard bearer.*

From The Conquest of Gaul translated by S. A. Handford

# Warrior Queen

In the following extract from Warrior Queen by Martin Mellett, the Roman Governor of Great Britain called Suetonius Paulinus orders his legions to attack a huge army of Celts led by Boudicca. During the battle, Morticcus of the Catuvellêauni tribe, who had once been a threat to Boudicca's leadership, was killed whilst helping to ensure her safety.

Boudicca too came among her people. As at Camulodunum, she rode in a chariot with her daughters by her side. She went from tribe to tribe, speaking with the warriors and laughing with their wives and children. Eventually she wheeled to a halt at the head of her vast army. 'Britons!' she yelled. 'I have not come here today seeking to avenge my lost wealth and kingdom. Instead, I come amongst you as an ordinary woman, fighting for my freedom and for my outraged daughters. The Roman greed has pushed us to the brink of our endurance... but the gods have decided to grant us a just vengeance. Paulinus' legions will not be able to withstand the yells and screams of our thousands, let alone the impact of our charge. Look what a pathetic few you are fighting. After today, we will be rid of the Roman yoke for ever – remember that, and you will crush them like insects in the first attack.'

A thunderous roar went up from the warriors and a forest of swords waved in the air above their heads. Boudicca discharged her daughters and the two girls crossed to the hillside to watch the battle commence. As usual, Morticcus joined his leader in her chariot, taking charge of the reins. The warrior Queen's war-cry rang out across the length of the narrow valley and struck a blade of fear into enemy hearts: 'Death to the Romans!' she screamed. Behind her, an ear-splitting chorus of one hundred and twenty thousand Celtic voices took up the cry. Boudicca's chariot lurched forward and the British charge began.

The screaming, yelling multitude shook the air and ground alike as they pounded their way up the long, shallow slope towards the enemy. On either flank groups of chariots bucked and bounced across the uneven grass. The Britons drove relentlessly onwards, filling the valley with charging bodies, their long swords flashing in the sun.

Roman knuckles whitened on the shafts of their javelins. Teeth gritted, they awaited their orders. The endless sea of Celts rolled towards them; irresistible, terrifying. Closer and closer. Louder and louder. Now the very earth trembled beneath the defenders' feet. Two hundred paces. Roman officers looked towards the hillside, where Paulinus sat astride his horse, sword lifted high in the air; cold and unmoving. One hundred paces. Suddenly Paulinus brought his sword sharply downwards. The officers turned and gave the order and the first volley of javelins was dispatched towards the enemy. A thousand missiles streaked across the face of the sun and whistled earthwards.

The front line of Celtic shields went up as if pulled by a gigantic string. A moment later, the swarm of javelins thudded home. Many of them shot clean though the leather shields. Other simply stuck in the outer skin. In both cases though, the soft iron shank behind the javelin-head bent and brought the lengthy shaft into contact with the ground. The front line of Celts now found themselves with useless shields. The bent javelins were impossible to pull out. To make matters worse their comrades behind were now crashing into them. In frustration, most elected to throw the shields away and charge on up the slope.

It was suicidal. The next volley of javelins, launched at fifty paces, streaked towards soft, undefended targets. The entire British front line shuddered and dropped – slaughtered to a man. The charge faltered. Paulinus, seeing his chance, gave the signal and his trumpeters sounded the advance. Short-swords drawn, shields across bodies, the Roman legionaries started down the slope at a steady, controlled run. They made contact. The Britons, already breathless from their long uphill dash, suffered the full impact of a perfectly-timed charge. Short-swords darted from behind their shields in stabbing, thrusting movements.

The Celts had no answer. They had little room to swing their cumbersome long-swords in the fury of the cramped melée. Buffeted by the Roman shields, they staggered backwards, crushed into an ever-tightening mass.

Fighting savagely from the platform of her chariot, Boudicca could see that her warriors were being hemmed in. It was sheer slaughter. She had no alternative. 'Withdraw!' she yelled. 'There's no room to fight! Withdraw!' But it was already too late. Paulinus had ordered his auxiliaries and cavalry to close in on the flanks. Now the Britons came under attack from three sides and the massacre began in earnest. Morticcus tried to wheel the chariot around. But the shock of the auxiliaries' charge prevented him from doing so. Boudicca, slashing wildly with her sword, was suddenly hooked from the chariot by a Roman horseman. She fell to the ground, her weapon knocked from her grasp. Morticcus leapt down to defend her. Boudicca scrambled to her feet. As the Romans pressed forward, Morticcus swung his sword in a wide semi-circle. 'Ride, Boudicca!' he yelled.

Somehow, the Iceni Queen managed to remount her chariot and bring it under control. She looked back for Morticcus, but was too late. He had already disappeared beneath a wave of Roman soldiers. There was nothing she could do. Tears of anger and frustration welled in her eyes. Once more she screamed to her warriors: 'Withdraw! Withdraw!'

But the Britons didn't – or couldn't – respond. For a long time, they tried desperately to fight their way though on to open ground, but the solid rows of pushing, jolting shields formed a wall which they weapons were ill-suited to penetrate. Thousands upon thousands fell to the lancing jabs of the Roman broadswords, without even striking a single blow for their cause. In the end, seeing comrades slaughtered like cattle, those who were able broke and fell back down the sloping floor of the valley. Behind them, Roman trumpeters sounded the pursuit.

Now the Britons paid a terrible price for their over-confidence. As they reached the end of the valley, they found themselves trapped by their own lines of carts and wagons. There was no room to move – let alone flee – between the tightly-packed vehicles. Within moments, the Romans were upon them. Before the carnage was done, eighty thousand Britons had fallen to the avenging Roman swords.

The battle was over, and Boudicca had lost.

*From The Warrior Queen by Martin Mellett*

# A new boy in town

The following two extracts are accounts of life in Roman Britain. Ten year old Victor, a slave, is being taken to work for a new master, Felix, who lives in the town of Calleva. He is worried about how he will be treated.

The cart rattled along the country road. In the back were 12 snorting pigs – and Victor. Victor was 10 years old, and he was a slave. Ever since he could remember, he had worked on a farm.

That morning, the farmer had sold Victor. Now he was travelling to his new master, Felix. Felix lived in Calleva. Victor had never been to a town before. All the way there, he wondered what it would be like. He also wondered if Felix would treat him kindly. Masters were allowed to kill their slaves if they wanted to. Victor was shaking with fright.

At last the cart rattled into Calleva. Victor gazed around in wonder. He stared at all the shops selling things he had never seen before. There was one shop where people were eating food.

'That's a restaurant,' said a 12 year old girl beside the cart. 'I bet you've never seen one of those before. Now get down and follow me, you smelly slave. Felix sent me to fetch you. I'm one of his most important servants!'

Victor trotted after her through the crowded streets.

'It's all so big and busy here,' Victor gasped.

'Hah! You should see London then,' cried the girl. 'That's about ten times as big as Calleva. There are only about 4,000 people in Calleva.'

Victor thought that the girl was a bit of a know-all. 'What's Felix like?' he asked.

'Oh, he's a very great man,' she replied. 'He helps the Romans to rule this part of the country, you know. Hundreds of years ago, people in his family used to be kings of the Atrebates. Felix is much better off than they were. They used to live in dreadful little huts; but now Felix has a beautiful Roman house in town, and a lovely farm in the countryside. Come on, slave. We're nearly at the house now.'

From Living in the Past by Haydn Middleton

# Fun and games

In this episode Victor wishes that he were at the amphitheatre enjoying the games, instead of cleaning out his master's stables. Marcus is Felix's son and Victor has to leave his work to play with him.

Victor was fed up. Most people were on holiday – but he had to clean out the stables. He could hear people cheering and roaring in the distance. They were all in the *amphitheatre*. That was a big stadium outside the town. Victor wished he was there too. He knew just what the people were watching.

First there were acrobats and jugglers. Then there were some boxing and wrestling matches. Some strange animals from faraway lands might appear, for the crowds to stare at. Then an English bear would be let loose. Hunters would chase it around the amphitheatre, catch it and kill it.

Later on, things got even more bloodthirsty. Cocks or dogs were made to fight each other, until one of them was killed. Felix always betted on which one would win. He usually lost lots of money.

Sometimes there were fights to the death between men. These men were called *gladiators*. Victor's brother had become a gladiator. Perhaps he had lost a fight, and been killed. Perhaps he had died in a battle with a starved wild boar or wolf. Victor did not know. He had no way of keeping in touch with his brother because he could not write.

Victor got on with his cleaning. He wished that he had as much fun as Felix and his family. Just the day before, they had all gone to a chariot race in a nearby field. On most days, they spent hours at the local baths. Venusta and Claudia went in the mornings, Felix and the boys in the afternoons. They exercised and played games in the yard, then they had cold, warm and hot baths. Afterwards they sat and chatted with their friends. Felix usually had a few drinks too, and lost more money playing at dice and board games.

Victor stopped working, and dreamed of being rich, and having lots of spare time. But he could not dream for long. Marcus had raced back from the amphitheatre. He dressed up like his favourite gladiator. Then he told Victor to pretend to be a savage boar. Victor sighed, but got down on all fours and snorted.

They had lots of pretend fights like this. In the end, Victor always had to let Marcus the gladiator win!

From Living in the Past by Haydn Middleton

# Marcus and the hare

**Setting**
The workshop of a Roman craftsman.
**Characters**
Narrator; Marcus, a craftsman; Fabius and Julius, his assistants; General Claudius; Metella, the General's wife; Ceres, goddess of plenty; Mars, god of war; Mercury, messenger of the gods; Venus, goddess of love and beauty; Hercules; Roman soldiers; Venus's attendants; a hare; dogs; Actaeon, a hunter; musicians.

**Scenery and props**
A work-bench; a bed; tools; Roman costumes; animal costumes or masks; percussion instruments.

**Production notes**
This one-act play for a class of seven- to eight-year-olds is based in Roman Britain and could be undertaken as part of a topic on the Romans. All the class can take part as actors or as accompanying musicians, playing percussion instruments at the side of the stage.

| | |
|---|---|
| **Narrator:** | In Cirencester, known as Corinium in Roman times, was found a mosaic floor, bearing the design of a hare. This play is our idea of why a hare was used in the mosaic. |
| | (*Enter Marcus and his assistants.*) |
| | Our story begins in the workshop of Marcus the craftsman. He and his men cut and shape the *tesserae* from which they construct the mosaic floors. |
| | (*Marcus examines the work of his assistants who mime cutting the tiles.*) |
| **Marcus:** | Very good, Fabius, but these need more work. |
| | (*Moves on to Julius.*) These will do for the 'Seasons mosaic'. |

| | |
|---|---|
| | *(Enter Claudius and Metella. Metella looks around disapprovingly.)* |
| **Claudius:** | *(Haughtily.)* Ah, Marcus. |
| **Marcus:** | *(Springing round and bowing.)* General Claudius! *(Fabius and Julius bow also.)* |
| **Claudius:** | Marcus, I have work for you. The building of our villa is complete except for the floor in the *triclinium.* |
| **Metella:** | We cannot decide upon the design of the mosaic. Which of the gods or goddesses can we choose? |
| **Claudius:** | We want you to create a design for us, Marcus. |
| **Marcus:** | *(Bowing again.)* It will be an honour, General. |
| **Claudius:** | Excellent! We will leave it to you. Good day, Marcus. |
| **Marcus:** | Good day, General. *(Exit Claudius and Metella. Marcus, excited, still bows.)* Work for General Claudius! |
| **Fabius:** | Such an important man! |
| **Julius:** | But what'll you do, Marcus? What about the design? |
| **Marcus:** | This is difficult. I must think hard. *(Walks towards front of stage, thinking.)* I'll choose one of the gods – but which one? *(Continues to walk up and down pensively.)* |
| **Narrator:** | Marcus thought for a long while. Fabius and Julius finished work and left the shop. |
| **Fabius/Julius:** | *(Together.)* Good-bye, Marcus. *(Exit Fabius and Julius. Marcus does not notice them go.)* |
| **Narrator:** | Marcus thought till he was too tired to think any more. Then he lay on his bed and fell asleep. *(Marcus lies on his bed.)* As he slept, he began to dream. |
| | *(The sound of bells is heard. Marcus, dreaming, sits up slowly. Enter Ceres, carrying fruit, dancing joyfully to centre stage. Bells stop.)* |
| **Ceres:** | I am Ceres, the goddess of plenty. I give the summer, fine fruits and flowers, wealth and fullness. Choose me for your mosaic, Marcus, for I represent everything good. |
| | *(Ceres dances off to the sound of bells. Military drum beats begin. Enter Mars and soldiers. They march in formation across the stage and stop at the |

**Mars:** side of the stage while Mars returns to centre. Drums stop.)

I am the god of war – Mars. *(Draws sword.)* The Romans pray to me as they go into battle and I give them great victories. Choose me for your mosaic, Marcus, for I am very powerful.

(Drum beats. Exit Mars and soldiers, marching. Sound of maracas. Enter Mercury at high speed. Runs from point to point, stretching and leaping.)

**Mercury:** Mercury is my name – messenger of the gods. Choose me, Marcus, I'm the fastest of all. *Choose me!*

(Exits. Chime bars. Enter Venus with attendants. They sit gracefully around her as she speaks. Chime bars stop.)

**Venus:** Your mosaic design should be of me, Marcus, for I am Venus, most beautiful of goddesses.

(Exit Venus and attendants to chime bars. Enter Hercules to slow drum beats, flexing muscles. Drum stops.)

**Hercules:** I am Hercules. I have great strength, enough to carry the whole world on my shoulders. Make me your choice, Marcus. I am Hercules.

(Exit Hercules to drum beats. Marcus stands and walks to front of stage.)

**Marcus:** I don't know what to do!

(The gods and goddesses re-enter and circle round Marcus.)

**Gods/Goddesses:** *(Chanting.)* Choose me ... *(Repeat six or eight times getting louder.)*

*(The hare leaps in, followed by barking dogs. Gods and goddesses leave in panic. Marcus jumps on to his bed. The dogs chase the hare till she crouches by work-bench. The dogs crouch round her, growling. She takes Marcus's hammer and threatens them with it. Enter Actaeon, swaggering.)*

**Actaeon:** Quiet! Here! Here! *(The dogs leave the hare and come to sit round Actaeon, panting.)* I am Actaeon, the hunter. You had better choose me, Marcus, or I'll set my dogs on you!

**Marcus:** But you're not one of the gods. You're only a hunter. I'm not going to make a design of you!

**Actaeon:** *(Angrily to dogs.)* After him!

(The dogs gather round the bed. They leap at Marcus. The hare jumps out to centre stage. She whistles to the dogs. They turn to see her. She makes faces at them and then dashes off stage. They chase the hare. Exit Actaeon, calling to the dogs. Marcus, astonished, steps down from the bed, coming to the front of the stage.)

**Marcus:** *(Sighing.)* Thank goodness for that! I'm safe. The

|  |  |
|---|---|
| | hare has saved me. Thank you, little hare! (The hare appears at the side of the stage, waves cheekily to Marcus and disappears again. Marcus smiles and returns wearily to bed.) |
| **Narrator:** | Marcus slept on till morning. When he awoke, he could remember the dream clearly. |
| **Marcus:** | *(Rising brightly from bed and coming to centre stage.)* I've got an idea. I won't put any gods in my mosaic. I will choose the hare because she saved me from the dogs. *Assistants return. They and Marcus start work.)* |
| **Narrator:** | So Marcus and his men went to work to make the hare mosaic. General Claudius and his wife were very pleased and paid Marcus well. He gained much fame as a craftsman and all thanks to the little hare! (Characters all return to take a bow with Marcus, assistants and narrator.) |

Anna Simon

# The hill fort

After watching the film, having a look
At the large-scale map and reference books
And seeing the heads of axes and hammers
Dug up on the site and in the Museum,
We went to the very spot
Where Ancient Britons and Romans fought
And somehow felt the Romans were still
Advancing across the valley towards the hill.

From our earthworks covered with grass
We felt we saw them coming far off;
And if the Romans again were there
After nineteen hundred years,
Being Romans, they would just ignore
All British Rail and the Electricity Board
Have built since they were here before.
Serve them right to smell the sewage farm
And have to dodge the buses and cars.

True, they never arrived at our fort:
Anyone not following the bus route
Soon gets lost in that huge new housing estate...
Did we hear the chimes of an ice cream van
Or a trumpet sounding retreat?

Stanley Cook

# Letter from a Roman soldier

Although Roman legionaries were not supposed to marry, many had 'unofficial' wives and children. The following is a copy of a secret letter dictated to a paid scribe by Roman legionary Tiberius, stationed on Hadrian's Wall, and addressed to his 'family' in Camulodunum (Colchester).

My Darling Flavia, we have been parted for too long now. I grow bitter at the delays and false news that greets my every enquiry as to when I can expect a transfer south. I know that I am voicing the feelings of many when I say that I hate this posting. If it isn't the ceaseless rain or the sleet that penetrates even my thickest tunic, it is the boredom of sentry duty that drives me to despair. Occasionally we see action when rebellious northern tribes fling themselves at the wall, but more often than not our days are filled with patrols and fatigues. Of these, cleaning the toilets is by far the worst duty. Maximus, our officer, he doesn't get his hands dirty, he just barks out the orders. Three times a month we have to strap on full kit – armour, weapons, cooking pots, camp building equipment, and march for thirty kilometres. If our feet are blistered or attacked by frostbite, this can be agony.

There's something about the landscape here that hardens the heart. It is rugged scrub land across which the wind blows relentlessly, even in summer. I still feel the cold even on days when the sun is strong. I suffer with lice too and no matter how hard I try to rid my tunic of these creatures, they always return. There are some pleasant times of course when my companions and I are in good humour. We joke and tell stories, visit the bathhouse and indulge in gambling.

Sometimes I ask myself, why did I join the Roman army? I know that the pay is good, I'm fed and clothed, and I wanted adventure, but stationed here at the very edge of the Roman empire, in this cold, wet, and misty land, I don't think that this was quite the adventure I had in mind. One day, when I complete my twenty-five years service, we will be married and I will take you to Rome. I shall buy some land with my pension and our sons will farm the soil and have no need to follow their father's footsteps.

Until that day, my dearest Flavia, I must content myself with thoughts of you, our children and home.

Tiberius

Brian Moses

# The taking of Silchester

We do not know exactly when or how the town of Silchester (Roman name: Calleva) fell to the Saxon invaders. We do know that for a long time after the Romans left Britain people continued to live in the towns they had built and to carry on life more or less as normal. However, by the end of the 6th Century AD the Saxons had taken control of the whole of Britain and most Roman towns fell into disuse. Not much of Silchester remains today save for ditches and mounds where the walls once stood but in nearby Reading Museum you can see a lot of objects that were found on the site.

The chief of the Saxon war band stood in the courtyard of what had once been the Roman public baths and smiled. Such a soft life these Britons led, he thought. No wonder we win such easy victories.

He turned as footsteps echoed across the faded mosaic floor. Aelfric, his most loyal and trusted retainer, approached and bowed his head quickly.

'Is it over yet?' the chief asked.

"Very nearly, my lord. We have taken the amphitheatre.'

'Then Silchester is ours. Listen.' He held up his hand. The screams of the dying Britons who had fled the walls of the town to make a final desperate stand in the smaller and more easily defended amphitheatre carried faintly into the decaying, overgrown courtyard.

The chief lowered his hand. 'And the rest of the garrison?'

'Dead or flown, my lord.' Aelfric looked at his master.

The chief pointed in the direction of a doorway which stood at the top of a short flight of steps at the end of the courtyard. 'Do you know what this was, this building?'

Aelfric shook his head. He was not interested in towns or the buildings in them. When the Saxons stormed a town it was to destroy the inhabitants and claim the outlying farm land, not to take it for themselves. Towns were cramped and unhealthy places and town life sapped a man's strength and his fighting spirit – as it had done to the Romano-Britons.

'It is rather a special building,' said the chief, glad of the chance to instruct his subordinate. 'That British slave you gave me, remember?'

Aelfric nodded.

'Useful fellow. Told me all about this place. At one time he even worked here.' He took Aelfric's arm. 'Let me show you how these people wasted their time.'

Aelfric thought it was a waste of his time. He had a job to do and he wanted to get it over with as quickly as possible. But he followed his lord.

They went up the flight of steps and halted before the doorway. It was surrounded by cracked brickwork and overhung with ivy.

'My slave worked here when he was a boy,' the chief announced. 'After the Romans left the people here kept the place going until they forgot how to work it properly. It finally closed about twenty years ago.'

Aelfric nodded patiently and wished that he had killed the Briton. In the short silence that followed he noticed that the shouts and cries from the amphitheatre had stopped.

'The courtyard we were standing in,' continued the chief, 'is where they used to play games.'

'Games, my lord? Fighting games?'

The chief smiled scornfully. He was enjoying this.

'Fighting? These people don't know what the word means – not any more they don't. No, they played games with small round objects. One person throws the object to another person who catches it and throws it on to someone else.'

Aelfric looked blank. He waited for the chief to continue.

'That's all, my friend. There is no other purpose to the game. They simply throw things at each other and catch them and throw them and catch them and so it goes on.'

Aelfric shook his head. 'The only things worth throwing are spears and the only things worth throwing them at are people or, failing that, targets.'

The chief led the way inside the building. The first room through which they passed was covered from floor to ceiling with small tiles which in turn were partially covered in a mossy green slime.

'After they tired of pointless games they undressed in here,' he said, passing quickly through a doorway which led into another tiled room. Here the ivy had forced itself through the windows and through holes in the ceiling where it had wound itself round the stone and marble columns which supported the roof. In the middle of the floor was a large rectangular hole. Like the rest of the floor it was covered in tiles though many were cracked and broken and there were patches of black mould everywhere. A faint irregular green line ran around the sides.

'This used to be full of water,' the chief said. 'They used to bathe in here.'

'There's a river not far away,' said Aelfric. 'What's wrong with that?'

'There is more to it. Come.' They edged round the outside of the long-empty pool and stopped outside yet another doorway.

'The rooms through here were kept warm by fires beneath the floor.'

Aelfric looked incredulous but he did not interrupt.

'First they would go into a warm room, then a hot room and then into a hotter room still. Here their bodies would be scraped with metal tools to remove the dirt and dead skin.'

Aelfric winced. Better to remain dirty, he thought, than to suffer so much discomfort.

'After that they would come back in here and jump into the cold water.' He pointed again at the pool. 'Before leaving they covered their bodies in olive oil.'

Aelfric had had enough. 'My lord, it ill becomes us to stay in such a place. My lungs yearn for fresh air.' His chief smiled indulgently and led them back the way they had come.

The air outside did not seem fresh to Aelfric for it was the air of a town but it was better by far than the atmosphere of dust and decay that hung inside the building.

As they walked out of the courtyard to where the horses were tethered the chief said, 'My friend, it is not to display my learning that I show you this.' Though in truth he was quite pleased with his lecture. 'I show it to you as a warning. To me, to you, to all of us Saxons.'

Aelfric stopped and turned and raised a questioning brow.

'The people who built such places were giants among men.'

Aelfric nodded. 'The Romans.'

'Aye, the Romans. They built a great empire and defeated our ancestors in battle many times.'

Aelfric looked back at the crumbling building. He tried to picture what it must have been like in the days of Rome's glory but it was too difficult. The Romans had long gone. Dust and ivy ruled now.

'Take heed, Aelfric, and avoid soft living, for this is what it comes to.'

'With winter fast approaching, my lord? There will be little time for that.' But as he looked about the wide cobbled street along which they walked and at the closely packed red brick houses on either side he thought, 'It must have been a good life for them'. For some of them anyway. Why else would they choose to live there?

He shook his head fiercely. 'My lord, let us move the men from here as soon as possible.'

'You are right,' said the chief. 'This place does seem to breed unhealthy thoughts.' He untethered his horse and climbed into the saddle. I shall return to camp. Tonight we shall celebrate. It is not a great victory but it is still a victory.'

Aelfric bowed and mounted also. But as he turned his horse in the direction of the amphitheatre he thought, 'Now I wonder what that was used for?'

Peter Hanratty

# The boar hunt

It was very early in the morning. A chilly mist hung round the farmstead, but Anted hardly noticed the cold. He was going on his first boar hunt today! He held his new hunting knife proudly. Anted's fingers traced the swirling decorations carved on its handle, and ran gently along its sharp blade. He thought that it was the best knife in the world.

'Right, men, we're off!' Cuno and the other hunters whistled to their dogs, picked up their spears and strode out of the farmyard. Anted hurried after them, anxious not to be left behind. They all set off towards the still-dark forest. Once among the trees, they moved stealthily along the tracks made by deer and wild boar through the undergrowth. The dogs ran backwards and forwards, busily sniffing at all kinds of enticing scents. Startled wild birds cawed and flapped overhead. Anted's legs were scratched and stung by brambles and nettles, but, in his excitement, he ignored the pain.

Suddenly, Cuno's best dog stood very still, sniffing the air. Cuno signalled to the hunters to stop moving and listen. The forest was strangely still and silent. Anted was frightened. He was glad he was not alone among the tall trees.

All at once, the silence was shattered as the dogs began to bark and bay, hurling themselves forward through the bushes. Anted gasped. Now he could see five or six wild boar in a clearing only a little way ahead. For a split second, the boar were too frightened to move. There was just time for Cuno to hurl his spear towards the nearest animal. The other men rushed forward, following the dogs with their spears at the ready. They killed three boars altogether. The rest escaped.

Later, Cuno showed Anted how to gut and clean the dead boar with his new hunting knife. They carried their quarry home, slung upside down between poles. Tomorrow there would be a great feast at the farm, with plenty of roast boar to eat.

From The Everyday Life of a Celtic Farmer by Giovanni Caselli

# Honey (Anglo-Saxon monologue)

Today I tasted honey for the first time. I walked into the hut to get warm by the fire. My mother was busy making something. She said it was called mead. I remember the grown-ups drinking mead at the last feast. It made them laugh and go red in the face.

Mother said she made the mead out of honey. She got this honey from the man who keeps bees, in exchange for two large fish my father caught yesterday. Mother said we also use honey to keep fruit from going mouldy. She let me dip my finger in to have a lick. 'Just one small one, because it's very precious, like gold!'

It tasted like nothing I'd ever tasted before. It tasted of flowers and sunlight and summer and gold. It tasted of firelight in the Great Hall in winter. It was like food for the gods.

When I grow up I'm going to keep bees, like the man who lives in the hut by the woods. Then I'll be able to lick all the honey I want.

Tony Mitton

# Lindisfarne AD783

The dragons came with
thunder in their bellies,
and spilled it on the beach.
There it charged a holy place;
horns hooked, a wild face, and
hair that raged like the sun.
The monks knelt; didn't run,
or fight, but felt
the wrath of Thor's hammer.
Plates, goblets, gold and treasure,
fit to feast on in Valhalla,
filled each departing dragon.
Survivors watched their monastery burn,
waited for the thunder to return.

John Lynch

# The Viking terror

There's a wicked wind tonight,
wild upheaval in the sea;
No fear now that the Viking hordes
Will terrify me.

(Anonymous) 7th-13th century

Vikings liked to write about their skill in war, and in the following poem,
a Viking called Egil Skallagrimson tells of a raid that he took part in:

'I've carried the bloodstained sword
And the slippery spear,
The raven at my right hand
As we raiders went forward.
Burning for battle,
We made their barns blaze.'

# Viking longhouses

Many Viking farmhouses consist of one long room with a slanting roof. These houses are known as longhouses and vary in size from 12 to 30 metres in length.

The houses that I visited were made from a range of different materials. Some of them had wooden walls of either planks or logs. Sometimes the walls were made of wattle and daub – sticks, covered with a mixture of clay, dung and straw.

Other houses had walls built of either stone or turf. Some roofs were thatched with straw. Others were covered with turf. A turf roof is heavy, so there were two rows of strong wooden posts inside to support it. The roof is strong enough to support a man's weight. In one place, where the house was built on slope, I saw a cow standing on the roof eating the grass!

Inside, in the middle of the house there is a fire pit, where the food is cooked. There is no chimney, just a hole in the roof. There are no windows either, so it is dark, smoky and smelly.

The Vikings do not have much furniture. The only person who has a chair or a bed is the chief. Everyone else sits on stools or benches.

They served me food on wooden bowls and dishes. They gave me a knife and spoon to use, but they do not use forks. We drank from wooden cups or beakers or from drinking horns, made from reindeer horns. I was offered milk and ale and a strong drink made from honey, called mead.

*From Viking Stories by John Foster*

# Summer: the cloak of the wind

Toki lives in the Viking town of Jorvik. One day he is delighted to discover that a new family is moving in to the empty house next door, and they have a son called Bard who has a sister called Drifa.
If you visit York today, have a look round the Jorvik Centre where you will be transported back to Viking days.

One lovely hot day, Toki and Bard slipped away from their homes and took Drifa down the street to the waterfront to see if any ships were coming in.

They were lucky – a big merchant ship was tying up at the waterfront. The children kept out of the way and a seaman jumped on to the waterfront with a rope. The seamen were tanned with sun and wind, and their clothes were stained with salt. A boy not much older than Bard and Toki was letting out a rope so that the big sail came down in a heap on the deck.

Old Karl, Toki's grandfather, was sitting on the waterfront with his old friend Eymundr. They had bought a barrel of herrings, and were gutting the fish to be dried as food for the winter. Overhead, gulls were wheeling and screaming, looking for titbits. The children stood near the old men and listened to their talk. They watched the crew unload.

The ship had sailed from Iceland to Norway, where the merchants on board had sold some of their cargo of woollen goods and smoked food. They loaded up with Norwegian cooking pots made of soapstone, and other goods. Then they sailed on to Denmark where they had sold some at the market town of Hedeby. There they had taken on Rhenish wine, from Germany, in big pale jars. There they also bought grindstones of specially hard German rock, so that grit did not get into the flour as it did if the grindstone was made of soft rock. They took on board barrels of herrings. So by the time they reached Jorvik they had a great variety of goods.

One Icelander had a big pile of grey woollen cloaks to sell. He was unloading them, but people who had gathered to see what the ship had brought were laughing at him. It was such a hot day that no-one felt like buying a winter cloak. Winter seemed a long way off.

Suddenly there was a stir among the crowd. A group of men came riding up, and the crowd parted to let them through. They were wearing brightly-coloured clothes. Their cloaks were fastened with shining bronze or silver brooches. They wore silver and gold rings and armlets.

One man in a scarlet tunic had a hawk sitting on his wrist as he rode. His hair was held back by a golden band that shone in the sun. Two hounds sat panting as he reined in his horse. He wore spurs on his heels. He was the king of Jorvik.

The king rode up to the ship. He noticed that the man did not seem to be doing any trading, so he said that he would buy one of his good warm cloaks. He paid the man with silver coins struck in Jorvik. As the king had bought a cloak, people thought they must be good, and everyone started snapping them up. People thrust coins and bits of silver at the Icelander. The children watched fascinated as he scratched each coin to check that it was pure silver, and weighed them on his scales. In hardly any time at all, the cloaks were all gone. The Icelander looked more cheerful, and went off to spend some of his money. The king and his men rode off. They were going hunting in the country outside the town.

The children threw bits of fish guts up to the seagulls, and then sat down to listen to what the old men were saying. The coming of the merchant ship had made them remember the fighting ships in which they had gone raiding when they were young.

'The Karlhofdi was the fastest,' Karl recalled, 'The "Man's Head" – and our leader carved the head on the prow himself.'

Eymundr could make up poetry in his head. He never wrote it down, but he could remember long poems. When he was young, he had made up poems about the brave deeds of kings in battles on land and sea. On his travels he had recited them before the kings, who had rewarded him with smart clothing, gold arm-rings and good swords.

Sometimes Eymundr would eat with Toki's family, and after supper he would recite some of his poems when they were sitting round the fire. In the poems about sea-battles (which Toki liked best) Eymundr never said 'ship', but used expressions that made people see the ship speeding over the waves: 'the horse of the gull's track', or 'the raven of the wind'. Everyone knew what he meant as they had often heard the expressions.

'There's no better sight,' said Karl, taking the last fish out of the barrel, 'than a longship with her sail hauled up, and the wind filling it.'

'Ah yes,' mused Eymundr, 'the sail, the cloak of the wind.' He got up to go home.

And always after that, when Toki and his friends saw anyone wearing a grey Icelandic cloak they used to think of the sail of a speeding longship, 'the cloak of the wind'.

From The Vikings: Fact and Fiction by Robin Place

# Beowulf fights with Grendel

Beowulf is an Old English epic poem based on Viking legends mixed with historical events in sixth century Denmark. The oral tale was brought to England by Danish invaders and finally written down by a single but unknown poet in the early eighth century. In the poem we find that Hrothgar, the Danish king on the island of Zealand, has built a great hall Heorot where his warriors can feast, but they have to abandon the hall because it is ravaged by the terrible monster Grendel. Beowulf arrives at the hall with fourteen warriors and challenges the monster.

As Beowulf and his companions entered Heorot, and looked round in wonder, the noise fell back in front of them. Watched by curious Danes, they walked up a silent clearing, right up to the king ensconced on his throne.

'Greetings, Hrothgar! I am Beowulf the Geat, Ecgtheow's son.'

'Ecgtheow's son?' Hrothgar's kind old face was creased and grey. 'You are welcome then, and so are your companions.'

'Is it true,' Beowulf demanded, 'this hall, even your own hall, is unsafe after dark?'

Hrothgar grimaced. 'Every day at dusk the talking must stop. Drinking must stop. Those still alive have to leave this hall.'

'I,' said Beowulf, 'am thirty strong. I am going to crush this monster in single combat.'

At once the hall began to ripple with excited cross-currents of sound. Hrothgar gazed at the young warrior, his eyes so full of light; then his own eyes glazed, you could tell he was travelling the green roads of memory. It's because of his father, Hrothgar was thinking; he's come because I once sheltered Ecgtheow, and paid off his feud, isn't that it? The king got up and grasped Beowulf's right hand.

'And I've heard this monster is so reckless he does without weapons,' Beowulf said.

Hrothgar's face crumpled in pain.

'I'll fight on equal terms, then. No sword...'

'Beowulf...' objected Hrothgar.

'...and no yellow shield. I'll grapple this fiend hand to hand.' Beowulf paused. 'Hygelac, my king, would expect no less.'

'Beowulf...' began Hrothgar, but the Geat cut him off a second time:

'And he should have this coat-of-mail if I die. This corslet made by Weland. Send it back to Hygelac.'

'As you ask,' said Hrothgar.

Beowulf shrugged. 'Who knows? Fate goes always as it must.'

'First,' said Hrothgar, putting a hand on Beowulf's arm and turning him round to face the Danish warriors, 'take your place at our feast. Eat and drink after your long journey.'

Then all the Danish warriors rose from their seats and, led by Hrothgar and his queen, made their way out of the hall and into the gathering dark, away to the safety of the outbuildings.

There was almost silence in Heorot.

The Geats looked round, they listened to the hall creak in the small night wind, and they began to lay aside their helmets and corslets.

Then each man took a bolster from one corner of the hall and found himself a sleeping-place.

'Leave him to me!' said Beowulf. 'I'll fight him hand to hand.'

The Geats lay down and spoke in low voices. Except for Beowulf, not one of them believed he would see the next day or dawn, or ever go back to his family and friends.

Through the dark night a darker shape slid. A sinister figure shrithed down from the moors, over high shoulders, sopping tussocks, over sheep-runs, over gurgling streams. It shrithed towards the timbered hall, huge and hairy and slightly stooping. Its long arms swung loosely.

One man was snoring, one mumbling, one coughing; all the Geats guarding Heorot had fallen asleep – all except one, one man watching.

For a moment the shape waited outside the hall. It cocked an ear. It began to quiver. Its hair bristled. Then it grasped the great ring-handle and swung open the door, the mouth of Heorot. It lunged out of the darkness and into the circle of dim candlelight, it took a long stride across the patterned floor.

Through half-closed eyes Beowulf was watching, and through barred teeth he breathed one word. 'Grendel'. The name of the monster, the loathsome syllables.

Grendel saw the knot of sleeping warriors and his eyes shone with an unearthly light. He lurched towards the nearest man, a brave Geat called Leofric, scooped him up and, with one ghastly claw, choked the scream in his throat. Then the monster ripped him apart, bit into his body, drank the blood from his veins, devoured huge pieces; within one minute he had swallowed the whole man, even his feet and hands.

Still the Geats slept. The air in Heorot was thick with their sleep, thicker still with death and the stench of the monster.

Grendel slobbered spittle and blood; his first taste of flesh only made him more ravenous. He wheeled round towards Beowulf, stooped reached out for him, and Beowulf...

Beowulf leaped up and stayed the monster's outstretched arm.

Grendel grunted and pulled back. And at that sound, all the other Geats were instantly awake. They grabbed their swords, they backed off, they shouted for Beowulf.

Grendel tried to break free but Beowulf held him fast. The monster snorted and tugged, he could feel his fingers cracking in the Geat's grip.

Now the great room boomed. Clang and clatter shattered the night-silence as Beowulf and Grendel lurched to and fro in their deathly tug-of-war. Tables and mead-benches were overturned, Grendel roared and snarled, and in the outbuildings Danes woke and listened in the darkness.

When the Geats saw that Grendel could not escape Beowulf's grip, they surrounded him and slashed at him with their swords.

Heorot flashed with battle-lights. Those warriors did not know that no kind of weapon, not even the finest iron on earth, could wound their enemy. His skin was like old rind, tough and almost hard; he had woven a secret spell against every kind of battle-blade.

Now Beowulf twisted Grendel's right arm behind his neck. He locked it and turned it, slowly he turned it, putting terrible pressure on Grendel's shoulder.

The monster bellowed and dropped to one knee. He jerked and his whole body shuddered and trembled. With superhuman strength he jerked again as he tried to escape Beowulf's grip, he jerked and all at once, his right shoulder ripped. A ghastly tearing of muscle and sinew and flesh; a spurting of hot blood: the monster's arm came apart from his body. Grendel howled. He staggered away from Beowulf, and reeled out of the hall.

The Geats cheered and shouted; they hugged one another; they converged on Beowulf.

Beowulf was gasping. 'I want to throttle him...'

'He's finished!' roared one Geat.

'....here and now.'

'Done for!' shouted another.

'I couldn't hold him... not strong enough...'

'Wherever he goes,' said a third companion, 'death goes with him.'

'I've done as I said,' Beowulf panted, 'and avenged Leofric.'

Until that very moment, the Geats were not aware that they had lost one of their companions. They listened as Beowulf told them what had happened when Grendel first came to the hall; and all their joy at the monster's death turned to anger and gloom at the fate of Leofric.

'Look at this hand!' muttered one man.

'Each nail like steel.'

'Each claw, I'd say.'

'Ten terrifying spikes.'

'Hand, arm and shoulder.'

'No man can withstand Beowulf...'

'...and no monster neither.'

Beowulf raised a hand and the Geats fell silent.

'Hang it up!' Beowulf said. 'Stick it up outside the door, under the gable. And then give Hrothgar news of my victory.'

Beowulf's companions hastened to do as he asked. One man climbed onto another's shoulders just outside the great door, and by guttering candlelight secured Grendel's grasp, bloodstained and battle-hardened, under the gable.

*From Beowulf edited by Kevin Crossley-Holland*

# Viking gods

The chief of Viking gods is called Odin. He is the father of all the other gods and rules the sky. He has a long white beard and only one eye. He traded his other eye for a drink from the well of wisdom.

Odin knows everything that is going on, because he has two ravens that can speak. They fly above the world, telling him everything that they see.

Odin rides a horse with eight legs, which can travel faster than the wind. His guards are two fierce wolves. Odin's magic is so powerful that in a split second he can stop a storm, or change himself into any animal that he wishes. Because he is so powerful, the Vikings are afraid of him.

The most powerful of Odin's sons is the god Thor. Thor has a magic belt which makes him very strong. He wears iron gloves and wields a huge stone hammer. It was Thor who led the gods in their fights against the evil giants from Giant-land. The Vikings know when Thor is riding across the sky. They say that the sound of thunder is made by Thor's chariot, and that the flashes of lightning are sparks from its wheels.

Not all their gods are clever and good. The most wicked god is Odin's brother called Loki. The other gods have punished him by chaining him to a rock. Above the rock is a monster, with poison dripping from its jaws. Loki's wife tries to catch the poison in a bowl. But she cannot catch it all. When a drop falls on Loki, he shivers and the earth shakes. According to the Vikings that is how earthquakes are caused.

There are many other gods, such as Frey, the god of love, marriage and growth. When the Vikings plant their seeds, they give Frey presents of bread and ale, so that he will look after the crops and make them grow.

*From Viking Stories by John Foster*

# Thor visits the land of the giants

This story is part of a Viking saga. It is about Thor, the god of thunder, and the journey he set out on to prove his strength. The journey and the trials of strength would have been very familiar to the Vikings.

One summer day, Thor, Loki and their two servants set off to visit Utgard, the land of the giants. After a long journey, they arrived at the gates of Utgard to find them locked. Thor thumped and hammered on the gates, calling out for someone to come and let them in, but Loki grinned and slipped through the bars, dragging the others after him. They walked into the great hall of Utgard. In the middle of the hall was a long table around which hundreds of giants were seated on benches, eating and drinking and making the most enormous noise. The giants all began to laugh as Thor marched up to the Giant King who was seated on a chair at the far end of the hall.

'Greetings, Giant King,' said Thor, politely.

The Giant King sat chewing bones and did not even look at Thor. From time to time he tossed a bone over his shoulder and picked up a new one.

Thor spoke again, a little louder:

'Greetings, Gi...'

The Giant King interrupted, 'So you're the great thunder god Thor, are you? Well, you look like a scrawny little piece of work to me. I suppose you've come to test your strength?'

Thor was furious at the Giant King's rudeness, but it did not seem a very good idea to lose his temper when he was surrounded by giants.

'What skill would you like to challenge us with?' continued the Giant King.

Thor looked around him at the giants.

'I doubt if anyone here can drink as much as I can,' Thor replied.

The Giant King signalled to a servant, who brought forward a huge drinking horn.

'This is the horn used by all my followers,' he said. 'A good drinker can finish it in one draught, and all here can down it in two at the most. Let us see what the great Thor can do!'

Thor took the horn. It was certainly not the largest he had ever drunk from. He raised it to his mouth and began to swallow. He felt sure he could drink it all, but he ran out of breath before the horn was empty. He looked into the horn and found that it was no less full than before. He drank a second time, and again had to stop for breath. This time the horn was no longer brimming full. He took a third draught, gulping down the liquid until he was sure he must empty the horn, but although the level was lower than before, the horn was no means empty.

'You don't seem to be much of a drinker,' said the Giant King. 'Why not try your strength? Some of the younger giants like to test themselves by lifting my cat. We don't think this much of a feat, but perhaps you'd like to try?'

Standing beside the Giant King's chair was the most enormous cat Thor had ever seen. He braced himself and then put both arms under the cat and heaved. The cat simply arched its back. Thor heaved again and managed to make the cat lift one paw off the ground before he had to admit defeat.

'As I thought,' said the Giant King scornfully. 'You may be strong in Asgard and in the realms of men, but your strength is nothing here.'

At this Thor grew angry. 'I can match any of your men in a fight. Just let anyone here wrestle with me.'

There was a roar of laughter from all the giants in the hall.

'Everyone here feels that wrestling with you would be too easy,' said the Giant King. 'Perhaps you could fight Elli, my foster mother.'

A wrinkled old woman hobbled forward leaning on a stick. Thor thought that the Giant King was making fun of him until Elli threw down her stick and took hold of him. He knew at once that his strength would be sorely tested. They struggled and fought, but eventually Elli threw Thor off balance so that he landed on one knee.

'Enough, enough!' shouted the Giant King. 'You have shown us that you have no strength as a wrestler either. As you pose no threat to us, you may eat with us and spend the night here in Utgard.'

Thor and his companions were very hungry and tired after their long journey. When they had eaten, the tables were pushed back, and they spread their bedding in a space on the floor among the giants.

Thor awoke early, before any of the giants, and roused his companions.

'Come, let's go before the giants wake up,' he whispered.

They tiptoed over the sleeping giants and out of the gates of Utgard. To their surprise, they found the Giant King already outside waiting for them. He walked with them across the plain for a while.

At last he stopped: 'This is where I must leave you. Thor, do not feel too badly about your failures last night.'

Thor was puzzled. 'But I have never before been so soundly beaten,' he said.

The Giant King replied: 'You were not competing in a fair fight. I feared your strength, so I used magic to deceive you. The other end of the horn that you drank from was in the sea. When you reach the shore you will see just how much you have lowered its level. The cat you lifted was really the giant serpent whose body is wrapped around the world. You managed to lift it until its back touched the sky. And as for Elli, it was a wonder you withstood her for so long. You see, Elli is Old Age, which defeats all men in time.'

Thor was furious that he had been tricked. He seized his hammer Mjollnir and swung it around his head, but the Giant King and Utgard had vanished, as if they had never been.

From The Vikings by Robert Nicholson and Claire Watts

# Odin's men

In ashen ships through hail and storm,
Over the foam, over the spray.
Taut cracking sails in wailing winds,
Over the spray, over the waves.
The sea wolves sail.

With beaten swords and hide bound shields,
Onto the beach, onto the shore.
They pound through the surf carrying strife,
Onto the shore, onto the strand.
And howl war-cries.

Crush the peace with their curdling chant,
Raiding the farm, raiding the church.
Grain and gold and life blood they steal,
Raiding the church, raiding the store.
In coats of mail.

Then to their farms to plough the clods,
Sing their sagas, pray to their gods.
Nurse their children, cuddle their wives.
Pray to their gods for peaceful lives.
Growl lullabies.

David Poulter

# Alfred the hero

In 870 King Ethelred of Wessex and his brother, Alfred, fought against the Viking host at Ashdown. The fighting went on till nightfall. Many men were killed, and the host fled. And two months later, Ethelred and Alfred fought against the host at Meretun. They lost this battle. And after Easter, in 871, Ethelred died. Then Alfred became king.

In Alfred's kingdom, there were nine battles against the host. In the end, the West Saxons made peace with them.

In 875, the host invaded Wessex again. The king made peace with them. They swore to him on the sacred ring that they would leave his kingdom quickly. And then they shared out the lands of Northumbria. They busied themselves with ploughing, and with making a living for themselves. And in the autumn of 877, they shared out some of Mercia too.

In 878, the host rode over Wessex. They drove many of the people overseas, and conquered most of the kingdom. But King Alfred and a few others made their way through thick woods to the marshes. And in the Easter after, they built a fort there at Athelney. Then, with the men from that part of Somerset, Alfred led raids against the host.

Then, in the seventh week after Easter, Alfred met all the men from Somerset and Wiltshire and part of Hampshire. And they were very glad to see him.

And two days later he went to Edington. And there his army fought against the whole host. They beat the host, and chased them all the way to their fort. Then for two weeks, they besieged the host inside the fort.

Then the host swore that they would leave the kingdom. They also promised that their king would become a Christian. And three weeks later, their king, Guthrum, came to Alfred. He was christened, and Alfred became his godfather. Then he stayed with Alfred for twelve days. And after that, the host went away from Wessex.

From Living in the Past: The Dark Ages by Haydn Middleton

# TUDORS

# Setting sail with John Cabot 1497

I'm Samuel Wright an ordinary seaman. John Cabot is my captain. He's a Bristol man, but a citizen of Venice with some Genoese blood in his veins so they say.

We are a crew of eighteen and all of us are Bristol men except for the captain's three sons Lewis, Sebastian and Sancho.

Cabot has obtained a charter from the king to try to find a way to Cathay and India. We're preparing to set sail this week.

I think the sea must be in my blood because being an ordinary sailor is no fun these days, even though some recent inventions do help a bit. I mean although our ship is fairly small we still have a rudder instead of a steering oar and the magnetic compass is much improved. You can always be sure of finding North now. We have printed maps instead of those drawn by hand which allow us to have more maps and of course there is the astrolabe which helps us pinpoint our position much more accurately. Mind you despite all these inventions our day to day existence as sailors is still terrible.

It's alright for the officers, not that we have many with this small crew, but nevertheless they live very comfortably in richly furnished cabins while we ordinary sailors have cramped, smelly, disgusting quarters in the forecastle of the ship. In fact there's barely enough room to lie down to sleep and sleep is what you crave when you've been up and down the rigging all day or the weather's bad. Sometimes the sea is so rough that everything down below is wet and there's always a stench of bilge water from the hold underneath.

It's not surprising that many seamen are rough violent men. They are used to long ocean voyages which are full of hazards like hunger, disease, shipwreck and piracy.

Life is hard, brutal and unhealthy. Disease spreads quickly in damp, filthy conditions. I've seen many sailors suffer from a skin disease called scurvy because there are no fresh vegetables to eat. The food is very poor. We live on bread, cheese, salted meat and fish which soon rots in the damp. I've often seen maggots in the bread and there's mould everywhere. We do have ale to drink but that's only because after a few days at sea the drinking water becomes stale and foul.

Despite all the hardships I'm very excited about this voyage. I love the feeling of adventure and the unknown. It'll be wonderful if we discover a North West passage to Cathay and the Indies.

I know that Cabot is one of the modern sailors. He's one of the growing number who, like Columbus, believe that the Earth is not like a flat plate but like a ball, a rounded sphere. I hope he's right.

I know this voyage will be harder than any I've undertaken before but I'm a strong man and eager for adventure. It would be wonderful to claim a new land for England. What tales I'll have to tell my children if I survive.

Cabot thinks he'll become a rich man by finding gold and silver through his discoveries and that the king will pay well. I hope he's not disappointed. Me, well I just want to be there, to be part of it all. I can't wait to set sail.

Margaret Blount

# Anne Boleyn

## A Legend of the Tower of London

Her little feet in scarlet shoon
They made a pleasant sound
Across the pavement where the moon
Drew patterns on the ground.

Her clenchèd fists so small and white
Went beating on the door,
The oaken door that to her sight
Would open, never more.

She knelt upon the grey cold stone,
And bowed her head in tears;
She wept, because her heart had grown
Too wild to hide its fears.

'O Harry love, O dear my King
I prithee let me in;
Thou couldst not do this cruel thing
To merry Anne Boleyn.'

She fluttered like some wounded lark
And ever called his name;
They chained her wrists and through the dark
They led her to her shame.

So young was she to die alone,
So fair, and full of tears,
So warm to rest beneath a stone
Through countless weary years,

That sometimes now men hear her feet
Across the tower floor,
Her voice beseech, her small hands beat
Upon that silent door.

'O Harry love, O dear my King
I prithee let me in;
Thou couldst not do this cruel thing
To merry Anne Boleyn.'

Barbara Bingley

# The day the Queen came to stay

Do you know the name of our Queen? She is called Elizabeth. You might have seen pictures of her in the newspapers or on television, so you know what she looks like. You may have been lucky enough to see her in person if she ever visited your town.

More than 400 years ago there was another Queen Elizabeth. She was the first Queen Elizabeth and we know about her from history books and pictures that were painted of her when she was alive.

She wanted people to see her and she also wanted to travel around the country seeing the towns, villages and houses where her people lived.

In those times there were no newspapers and no television so the people who lived all over England did not know what was happening in other places. There were no cars or trains either so they could not go to London to see the Queen because it would take a long time to walk or go on horseback.

One summer day long ago, everyone that lived in the small town of Kenilworth was very excited because Queen Elizabeth was coming to visit. The sun shone brightly and everyone was really busy getting things ready. Young John, one of the boys that worked in the big kitchen at the castle, was specially excited. The cook had told him that if he finished all his work he could go outside and watch as the Queen's procession came through the castle gates.

John's job was to turn the handle of the roasting spit over the log fire in the huge fire place. The spit was a long pole with spikes to hold the meat. There were chickens, pheasants, a goose and a whole pig to be roasted over the fire. John had to keep turning the handle of the spit so that all sides of the meat were cooked. One of the cooks poured hot fat over the meat as it turned. The fire was so hot that poor John felt as though he was cooking too. He sat there turning and turning as the cook took the cooked meat off and put more uncooked meat on the spikes.

Other cooks were cutting up vegetables, making bread, chopping herbs, washing fruit and beating eggs and milk to make custard. All the time, everyone was shouting, laughing, talking and running backwards and forwards getting everything ready for the great feast. It would take all day but everything would be ready for the evening when the Queen and the Lords and Ladies sat at the long wooden tables in the Great Hall.

At last John could go outside. The sun was still shining although it was after seven o'clock in the evening. As he reached the gates, there were crowds of people pushing and shoving to get a look at Queen Elizabeth as she rode on a big white horse through the gates.

She was so beautiful in her white and gold dress which was covered with jewels. She had pearls around her neck and in her curly red hair. There was a ring on each of her fingers. John looked at her pale white face and then she smiled as everyone cheered. He noticed that her teeth were black. He had seen other people's teeth like that, but he had expected the Queen to have nice white teeth.

But still she was very proud and grand, more than all the other Lords and Ladies that followed behind her. Lord Robert Dudley, who owned the castle and was a great friend of the Queen, was there to greet her. Then there was a great fanfare of trumpets as she rode under the archway that had been covered with flowers of every colour. Next there were people playing flutes, others reading out poems and girls dancing and singing specially for their Queen.

As she was led into the castle, there was a great blast from the guns to salute her, followed by fireworks shooting up into the sky, sparkling and glistening in all the colours of the rainbow. John watched as the fine Lords and Ladies went into the castle building ready for the feast. He was not allowed to see the tables piled high with wonderful food. He would not be able to listen to the music, nor watch the dancing because he was just a poor kitchen boy.

*Marlene Greenslate*

# High seas adventures

Martin and Margery Swallow listen eagerly to their father, Captain Swallow, as he tells of his adventures on the high seas with his friend Captain Francis Drake.

'But tell us of your voyage, sir. Did you get to the West Indies?'

'We got there,' Captain Swallow answered, 'but it's a miracle we came away. We'd been first to the coast of Africa and taken slaves there. We shipped them across to Dominica, an island in the Spanish Main where we sold them there. Then our troubles began, eh Drake? We sailed on to other islands and took some plunder, but one of the ships we had from the Queen was in very bad shape. She wasn't in good condition when we sailed, was she, Drake?'

'No,' the visitor took up the tale, 'the *Jesus of Lubeck* had seen better days, but the Queen lent her to us so we had to take her. Her timbers were rotten, and she was far too old for such a voyage. The *Minion* was the other Queen's ship and she was sound enough, so was my little *Judith*, as snug a bark as you could hope to find for all she's only sixty tonnes.'

'Thank God for her,' Captain Swallow said gravely, 'but for her I might not have come safe home.'

'Oh Father,' Martin exclaimed, 'don't say the *Matthew* is lost?'

'Aye, my boy, at the bottom of the sea with another good ship.'

'How did it happen?' Master Tidmarsh asked.

'The weather was dreadful, blowing a storm for four days. We'd sailed into the gulf of Mexico, hoping to pick up some of the treasure that is there for the taking in those lands. You understand the Queen lends us her ships and we give her a share in what we take, so we didn't want to go back with empty holds. Well, the storm damaged the *Jesus* so badly that we were beginning to think of abandoning her altogether. We were driven along, finding no place to shelter and Sir John Hawkins, who is Captain Drake's cousin and, as you know, commanded the expedition, was having a bad time aboard the *Jesus*. We came to the port of Mexico, a place called San Juan de Ulua. We stood in there and thankful we were to make harbour.'

'But we only had one quiet night,' Drake put in. 'We'd barely begun the repairs we so badly needed when a Spanish fleet of great ships, about thirteen of them, arrived outside.'

'Oh!' Martin exclaimed. 'Then you were trapped in the harbour?'

'Aye,' his father nodded. 'But we sent word to the Spanish admiral that we wouldn't allow him to enter without his promise not to harm us. We were fewer than them and in poor shape but we commanded the entrance. The weather was still so bad, and there's no other port along that coast, so he had to deal with us. The entrance is narrow and we had our guns, you see. Anyway, he gave his word and then we let the ships in.'

'We trusted him, but I'll never trust the word of a Spaniard again,' Captain Drake said fiercely, 'for no sooner had we let them in than they attacked us. There was a hot battle, I can tell you. The *Jesus* had her masts shot away by their guns and was unable to move, and two of our ships were captured.'

'And my poor little *Matthew* was battered and pounded.' Captain Swallow took up the story. 'A great hole was blown in her side but I and a good few of the crew managed to get off in boats, more of my fellows jumping into the sea and swimming for the *Judith* which was nearest to us. We managed to get a lot of our goods into the boats, thank goodness. Sir John Hawkins had to leave the *Jesus* and he got aboard the *Minion*. The Spaniards had sent fire ships among us and that was how we lost the other two.'

'Then they are our enemies,' Martin said, 'whether we're supposed to be at war with them or not.'

'They are indeed,' Captain Swallow answered. 'After what happened at San Juan I shall attack every Spanish ship I find on the high seas, aye and take her plunder as she took ours, won't you, Drake?'

'I swear I will,' the visitor answered. 'The sea is for all and they have no right to claim that west from the islands of the Canaries is all theirs.'

'How did you get away?' Master Povey asked gravely.

'Only the darkness saved us,' Captain Drake told him. 'Then, praise be to God, the *Minion* and my *Judith* slipped out of the harbour into the open sea. We had to abandon the *Jesus* which was beyond help, and laden with treasure too, and a lot of the poor fellows aboard must have been taken prisoner when the Spanish boarded her. So out of six ships only two got free. Captain Swallow and I lost sight of the *Minion* in the dark. We made all speed we could and didn't see her when morning came. We were short of provisions and there were no full stomachs, I can tell you. Many of the poor fellows aboard took sick and died.'

'Aye,' Captain Swallow went on. 'We'd taken aboard so many from the ships that sank and we'd had no time to load up with fresh food and water. But somehow we got home to Plymouth harbour and here we are. What a journey, eh Drake?'

From The Spanish Boy by Juliet Dymoke

# Watching the Armada sail past

Kit, his father and his friend Nick catch their first glimpse of the Spanish fleet as they sail past Portrue, then witness a skirmish between English and Spanish vessels.

Outside Plymouth, the English seamen caught their first glimpse of the Armada.

Seven hours later, in the grey Sunday dawn, Kit was scrambling into his clothes, his heart pounding to the reverberation of the guns.

'They're at it, boy,' his father shouted up the attic stairs.

His voice sounded oddly young – just like Dick's.

'... The two fleets are engaged. Come thou down quickly and saddle the cob.'

Once out in the half-shadows, scrambling up to the beacon beside the trotting horse, Kit gasped at the terror and the beauty of the hour. The western darkness flashed with flame and, as he mounted higher and saw the Channel stretching far away south to the sky above France, the whole world seemed to roll with an interminable thunder.

Nick was up there before them, looking white and astonished.

'Drake's giving them a warm welcome,' Sir Roger shouted up to him.

Just then the gusting wind caught the roar of battle and blew it down smack on Portrue like the crack of an explosion.

Kit covered his ears.

'Won't everyone be blown up?' gasped Nick, as the gust blew away.

But Sir Roger made no answer. He was scanning the empty bay with his keen seaman's eyes.

'Here they come,' he shouted at last. 'Look, Kit. Look, Nick. A mile out from Trap Head.'

Both boys strained their eyes to the western headland.

'One....two....' shouted Kit, seeing the high forecastles and the billowing sails of the Spanish galleons.

'No. Five... Six,' exclaimed Nick. 'No more. They're all coming on in a bunch.'

Before their astonished gaze, the massed might of King Philip of Spain came slowly into view, sailing in a close-packed arc, pointing east up the English Channel.

Then the guns flashed out again and, a moment later, the deafening roar of the cannons and the demi-cannons echoed and re-echoed across their peaceful bay.

'But where's *our* fleet?' cried a familiar voice over the dying din. 'Where's our Dick?'

Kit turned to see his mother standing behind him with half the village at her side.

As if in answer, a hundred pin pricks of fire lit up far out to the southwest. And with the booming sound from the English guns came the rending of timbers and the cries of seamen from the Spanish ships.

'They're to the windward,' shouted Sir Roger in triumph. 'They're coming in on a good south-wester. They've got the Spaniards on the run.'

Yet, as Kit watched the slow, stately sailing of the enemy up the Channel, it did not seem to him that they were 'on the run'. A sail was torn, a mast was splintered yet on came the great arc of galleons and hulks, unhurried and undeterred.

Nick could hardly believe his eyes.

'With all that noise,' he blurted out, 'I thought they'd all be sunk.'

The sun was now well up in the sky, and back on the farms there were tasks to be done. Yet, as Kit turned again to where his mother stood, he saw that more and more of the villagers had come crowding to the cliff-edge. They were standing agape at the pomp of Spain.

From When the Beacons Blazed by Hester Burton

# The aftermath of the Armada – a famous escape

Over a year after the defeat of the Armada a gentleman in Spain received a letter from a friend in Antwerp. The friend was Don Francisco de Cuellar, who was thought to have died in a wreck off the coast of Ireland.

When Cuellar's ship with two others had been swept into Sligo Bay, they dared not risk a landing. Ireland was wild and unruly, and English soldiers patrolled the coasts, fearing a Spanish invasion. A severe storm drove the three ships onto the beach, and over 1000 men drowned. Cuellar grabbed a hatch cover and was swept onto the shore, smashing his leg on a timber.

Half-naked, shivering and covered in blood, he escaped the plundering Irish and made for the woods. A beautiful girl fed him, although she took his Order of the Holy Trinity from his neck. He was helped by a priest in disguise, with whom he conversed in Latin. Then, gathering more fugitive Spaniards, he found safety in Rossclogher Castle, home of Dartry, Chief of the MacClancy clan.

The English Lord Deputy, Sir William Fitzwilliam, had raised an army of 1700 men to exterminate the Spaniards and punish their Irish helpers. The MacClancys could not hold out against such a force, so they fled to the mountains. Cuellar and his twelve companions remained to defend the castle, armed with four boatloads of stones, six muskets and six crossbows. The castle, set in a bog and partly surrounded by water, was difficult to attack. After seventeen days, a bitter snowstorm sent the English marching back to Dublin. The MacClancys returned and Dartry offered his sister in marriage to Cuellar, begging the Spaniards to stay. But Cuellar was intent on getting home to Spain.

With four companions he left the Castle secretly before dawn. He ran into some English soldiers, but once more he was rescued by women who hid him. Eventually he met a bishop who smuggled him, with other Spanish fugitives, to Scotland. A Scottish merchant took him to Flanders where the Duke of Parma was paying five ducats for each returned Spaniard. His luck held to the end. Though marauding Dutch flyboats sank his ship, he scrambled ashore at Dunkirk: one of three who survived out of 270 Spaniards who went down with his ship.

From The National Trust Book of the Armada by Mary Connatty

# An inventory

In Tudor times, when people died, everything they had left
behind was listed on an inventory.

The Inventory of all the goods and chattels which were Richard
Newhouse's of More Lane, Great Crosby at the day of his death, viewed
and priced by these men – Nicholas Johnson, James Tarleton, John
Ridgate senior and Thomas Fletcher – 10th July 1590.

| | |
|---|---|
| One yoke of oxen | £4.34p |
| One cow and a calf | £2.00p |
| One heifer | £1.50p |
| One other cow and a calf | £2.00p |
| One horse | .66p |
| One mare | .70p |
| One colt | .12p |
| One young swine | .17p |
| 2 geese | .05p |
| A cock and 5 hens | .10p |
| Barley upon the ground | £3.66p |
| Beans and peas | £1.00p |
| Grass for hay | .50p |
| A wain and a cart | .20p |
| A pair of wheels | .25p |
| Harrow, plough and equipment | .17p |
| 2 yokes | .25p |
| A spit, golbarts and iron pin | .40p |
| One axe | .03p |
| One fork and a spade | .04p |
| An iron rack, tongs and pothooks | .05p |
| Turf | .32p |
| Hemp growing | .66p |
| Brass and pewter | £3.00p |
| A frying pan | .04p |
| 2 little coffers | .10p |
| Treen* vessels | .10p |
| Earthern vessels | .05p |
| Bedstocks | .05p |
| In bedding | £1.33p |
| His clothing | .33p |
| 2 shelves | .10p |
| A simple board | .02p |
| A swine trough | .01p |
| 2 cushions | .04p |
| | |
| Total | £24.34p |

*wooden

# Doctor Kelly's cures

Kerry and Joe discover the long-lost village of Cleedale which mysteriously disappeared beneath the waters of a lake in 1589. Time has stood still in the village and in the following extract, Kerry and Joe meet up with Doctor Beamis Kelly who is attempting to find a cure for Grandma Mary's ailments.

'What about me? When are you going to cure my ills?'

'One moment, one moment,' said Doctor Kelly, picking up his black case and laying it on the table next to her chair. 'First, I think, the ague.'

'What is ague?' asked Kerry.

'Oh, a horrible illness, to be sure,' said the Doctor. The sufferer is afflicted alternately by hot, sweaty flushes followed by the shivers, so extreme that the teeth rattle in their sockets.'

'Sounds like flu,' said Joe.

'We take a paracetamol for that,' said Kerry.

'Parrots what?' said the doctor.

'It doesn't matter,' said Kerry.

'What do *you* do?' asked Joe.

'I,' said the doctor pompously, 'follow the advice of the great French physicians of the day.' And so saying, he unlocked his case. Inside, it was lined with royal-blue velvet and divided into innumerable tiny compartments. He pulled out a small silver box from one of them and laid it ceremoniously down on the table. Next, he took out a crystal bottle filled with a deep-orange syrup. He unstoppered the bottle in preparation and placed it next to the silver box. What was to happen next occurred in only a matter of seconds, so swiftly, in fact, that Kerry and Joe could scarcely believe what they had just witnessed.

'Here we go, then,' said Dr Kelly, flicking open the silver box and carefully removing its occupant: a large black spider. This he placed on a spoon taken from his case. To prevent it from running away, he pressed down on two of its legs with his index finger. Then, with remarkable dexterity, he poured the syrup from the bottle into the spoon, completely covering the spider with the sticky substance, and popped the whole lot in Grandma Mary's waiting, open mouth.

Kerry and Joe were so surprised, shocked and sickened by what they saw that they were never to forget it for as long as they lived.

'That's disgusting,' said Kerry.

'It's the best treatment I know,' said Dr Kelly.

'Well, thank God you're not my doctor,' said Kerry.

'Another *very* good reason for leaving Cleedale,' said Joe.

The doctor's visit was only half-over, however. There was still the problem of the gout. He replaced the bottle and box and pulled out a larger casket.

'What's in that, cockroaches?' said Joe.

'What, for gout? Don't be ridiculous, young man,' said the doctor. 'We can see how much *you* know. Gout is a very tricky complaint. Often we recommend bleeding to remove the poisons – the leeches, you understand. But I think this morning, something a little less severe.'

Kerry turned away. She felt distinctly ill just thinking about what the box might contain. She looked over to Grandma Mary, but the sight of the old woman sitting there licking her lips made her feel even more sick.

'Oh, you're not going to make her eat those,' she heard Joe saying, and looked round despite herself.

The casket was full of a line of dead mice, all lying rigid in death like a box of cigars.

'Eat them!' said Doctor Kelly, shocked. 'Most certainly not.'

He took out one of the mice and laid it carefully on a silver tray. Then, with the precision of a surgeon, he sliced the mouse in two with a single stroke of his scalpel.

'Right, feet up,' said the doctor to Grandma Mary.

She did as she was told, and when her feet were resting on the footstool, he carefully laid the two halves of the mouse on her swollen ankles.

'And that's meant to be good for arthritis, is it?' said Joe.

'Half a what?' said the doctor.

'For gout.'

'Indubitably', he replied.

Perhaps it was shock, perhaps it was the thought that she might get some illness and have to be treated by Beamis Kelly. For whatever reason, Kerry suddenly got a fit of the giggles. The sight of the yellowed old woman sitting there with her feet sticking out in front of her, half a dead mouse on each foot and a live spider inside her, began to amuse her. And then she heard her brother humming an old song their mum had sung to them both when they were younger and the laughing got all the louder.

'I know an old lady who swallowed a spider,
That wriggled and jiggled and tickled inside her.
She swallowed the spider to catch the fly,
I don't know why she swallowed the fly;
Perhaps she'll die.'
And Joe started to laugh too.

'I don't know what you two find so amusing,' said Dr Kelly. 'Mice have all manner of healing properties,' he continued, with as much dignity as he could muster. 'For instance, fact number one: if you have warts, just lay a half mouse on them for half an hour and then bury it. As the mouse decomposes, so the warts will disappear.'

Fact number one started both Kerry and Joe laughing even harder.

'Fact number two: if you've got a really bad case of the toothache, you could do a lot worse than eating a mouse which has been appropriately flayed and beaten.'

Kerry clutched at her stomach. She looked around the room at the expressions of the various members of the Cartwright family. Their seriousness only made her laugh all the more.

'Fact number three, and a tip for you, young lady,' said Beamis Kelly. 'If you want your eyelashes to grow thicker just take some young mice which have been beaten into small pieces, mixed with old wine, and boiled, and apply them twice a day.'

'Oh...ol...old wine, you say?' said Joe, trying to get the words out while holding his stomach and laughing. Tears were streaming down his cheeks.

'I think I'll stick to mascara,' said Kerry.

'And, of course, the burnt heads of mice make the base of an excellent powder for the scouring and cleansing of teeth,' continued the good doctor.

'Poor little mice,' said Kerry, regaining control a little.

'Oh, mice aren't the only animals which are used to benefit mankind,' said the doctor, and he tapped at various bottles and boxes in his case. 'Potions and syrups for all manner of complaints,' he explained. 'Dead moles are good as a cure for baldness, armadillo tail for deafness, and for leprosy there is some debate at present under way as to whether elephants' blood or the ashes of weasels are more efficacious.'

If they had thought that their laughing fit was nearly over, the new list of sure-fire cures got them going again.

'You know where you get all these things from, don't you?' spluttered Kerry.

'Where?' asked Joe.

'The Bodies Shop!' said Kerry, and burst out laughing again.

'My stomach, my stomach,' groaned Joe.

'Cramp, is it?' inquired Dr Kelly. 'Elk's hoof is what you need for that.'

'Stop it, stop it, stop it,' pleaded Kerry. 'No more. I can't stand it.'

'Well,' said the doctor primly. 'I can't force those to learn who will not,' and he snapped his case shut. 'Leave those on for another thirty minutes,' he said, gesturing towards the slices of mouse.

Kerry started to snigger again.

'And now,' said Dr Kelly, 'I shall take my leave of you all.'

Grandma Mary slipped a ten-shilling coin, called an angel, into his hand in payment for the treatment. He pocketed it deftly.

'Good morning to you, Doctor,' said the rest of the family meekly.

'Farewell,' he said, and flounced out of the house.

From The Weather Witch by Paul Stewart

# Bartholomew Fair

Bartholomew Fair was held from Henry II's time up until the mid-nineteenth century at the priory of St Bartholomew in London every 24 August. A lively description of the fair in the seventeenth century is given in Ben Jonson's Bartholomew Fayre.

**Chorus:**
ROOM FOR COMPANY, HERE COMES GOOD FELLOWS,
ROOM FOR COMPANY IN BARTHOLOMEW FAIR.


Cobblers and broom-men, jailors and loom-men,
ROOM FOR COMPANY IN BARTHOLOMEW FAIR,
Botchers and tailors, shipwrights and sailors,
ROOM FOR COMPANY, WELL MAY THEY FARE.

Paviers, bricklayers, potters and brick-makers,
Pinners and pewterers, plummers and fruiterers.

Colliers and carvers, barbers and weavers,
Pointers and hosiers, sailmen and clothiers.

Bell-founderers, fell-mongers, bellows-menders, wood-mongers,
Pump-makers, glass-makers, chamberlains and mat-makers.

Collar-makers, needlemakers, button-makers, fiddle-makers,
Fletchers and bowyers, drawyers and sawyers.


Anonymous

# Thomas

Thomas was aged eight when his mother,
Ursula Kemp, was hanged as a witch.
He was questioned at her trial at
St Osyth's, Essex.

I can hide here in the reeds;
They are never still or quiet.

*They have taken my mother;*
*They say she is a witch.*

Damp seeps up from the marsh;
There is nothing firm under me.

*They say she is a witch;*
*And they came to take me too.*

Darkness creeps through the reeds
And laps at the sky's blood.

*And they came to take me too*
*So that I could speak against her.*

There are noises around me;
They are rustling closer and closer.

*So that I could speak against her*
*And tell of her cats and her herbs.*

I want my mother to hold me;
I want her to keep me safe.

*Because of her cats and her herbs*
*They have taken my mother.*

Michael Harrison

# A Tudor criminal: Ned Browne

Ned had good, honest parents who brought him up well and gave him a good education, but he was a deceitful boy from earliest youth and was soon engaged on a career of shoplifting. He got into bad company very quickly and learned the art of cutting purses. In Tudor times, people kept their money in purses that hung from two strings attached to the belt. A man with a sharp knife in the palm of one hand would bump into a likely looking chap, draw the knife across the purse-strings, and the purse fell with a pleasant chink into his other hand, held ready below.

That was one way of making money, but Ned soon found others. He would see a rich lady with a purse at her belt and go up to her as if she were an old friend, put his arms round her and kiss her warmly. When she had escaped from this bear hug she would no doubt slap his face and he would apologise, say he had mistaken her for someone else and go away red-faced, but with the purse in his possession. In a crowd, a gentleman could have his money stolen by two cut-purses, one dropping a key or something in front of him and jostling him, and the other taking the purse. The gentleman would hotly accuse the man who had dropped the key, who would let himself be searched to prove that the gentleman was mistaken. Later, the thieves would share the booty – if the one could find the other, that is.

Ned got up to all sorts of tricks. He posed as an alchemist able to turn lead into gold, but needing money to build a laboratory – and some fool always put up the money in the hope of a rich return. He used the same disguise to sell love-potions of coloured water or deadly poisons to use on your enemies. At other times, Ned pretended to be a travel agent, offering to set up a wonderful trip abroad for a young gentleman but needing to have an advance of the money first, of course. Sometimes he disguised himself as a rich man and showed forged documents to prove that he was owed great sums of money that would shortly fall due. Pretending he needed ready cash in a hurry for a venture abroad, Ned would sell these documents at a reduced price to some poor fool who would then try to reclaim the money, only to find there was none due. Or, of course, he could simply play cards or dice, using his own specially doctored pack and loaded dice.

If the going got too hot, Ned could always slip across to France for a while, but he was such a master at disguise that he was very rarely known. He even possessed a false tail to disguise his horse. This horse once gave him a great adventure, which he boasted about till the day of his death. He was riding into Berkshire one day when he met a fat priest. Having been well educated, Ned could make himself acceptable to all types of company, high and low, and the priest quite took to him. Ned also took to the priest, for he saw that he carried a large sum of money in a cap-case attached firmly to his saddle. The priest, who said he was going to buy some land, admired Ned's horse greatly and as they rode along they bargained for an exchange. Eventually, Ned agreed to accept the priest's horse and nearly £7 in cash in return for his own fine horse. When they stopped for a meal Ned made an excuse to go to the stable and there he tied a hair tightly round his horse's leg, using a special knot that he could quickly undo. After the meal they exchanged horses and rode on, but soon the priest's newly acquired horse began to limp. The priest grew angry and said Ned had given him a bad bargain, but Ned replied that the priest must be riding incorrectly and offered to ride her for a few minutes to see what the matter was. So once more they exchanged horses, but did not bother to change saddles. Ned bent down and felt the horse's leg, loosing the hair; then he mounted and rode off, the horse going perfectly. Ned rode faster and faster, and soon the priest's shouts grew softer and softer, until he could no longer hear them and quite forgot him! However, like so many of his friends, Ned ended up on the gallows.

From Tudor People by John Fines

# Will Martin's diary

These diary extracts are from the Diary of Will Martin, a fictional account of a ship's boy, serving on the Disdain in 1587.

**September 6**

This is the last night I shall sleep in this house, for tomorrow I shall be at sea with my Uncle Edward on his ship, the *Disdain*. He is the Ship's Master. We sail for France on the dawn tide with a cargo of wool.

This will be my first voyage as Ship's Boy. I shall keep this journal just like my uncle keeps a ship's log. I never thought I'd get my chance so soon! I am not even ten, yet I will be a seaman!

I miss my family very much, especially my sister Kate, but I had to leave them to get work. The winter was so bad last year that we would have starved if I hadn't. I was lucky because my uncle said he would take me to work as a servant in his house in Plymouth. It was all so strange here at first. The town is so big and busy all the time compared to the farm. I was scared and lonely. I nearly ran back home in the first week because I was so homesick. I've been here now for eight months helping in the kitchen and running errands but now I'm going to do proper work. I've always wanted to be a Ship's Master, not just carrying cargo around the coast but crossing the oceans and fighting battles.

When I first came to Plymouth I begged Uncle Edward to let me start on his ship, but he just kept saying I was too young and I didn't know how hard it would be. He's only taken me on now because his own Ship's Boy died last week. He slipped on the rigging, fell into the harbour and drowned before they could get him out. Uncle Edward needed a new Ship's Boy quickly, so he finally let me take the boy's place. He told me that I must not call him Uncle Edward but Master when I am on the ship and he said I would be treated just like the rest of the crew. There would be no favours. That scared me a little because he sounded so hard but I'm sure he will take care of me and it will be exciting to sail with him.

**September 7**
We are about to leave harbour. The *Disdain* seemed very big when I first saw it, but now I'm on board there is very little room to move. Everything has to be stowed away neatly. It is very difficult to walk from one end of the ship to the other without tripping over something. We sleep below deck and it is dark and smelly down there. The men have to stoop so that they don't bang their heads, but I am small so it's not so bad for me.

**September 11**
I've been terribly sick for four days now and no one helped me – not even Uncle Edward! They just left me to lie on the deck with a sack over me and a bucket by my side to be sick into. It started soon after we had sailed out of the Sound and the ship started pitching and rolling on the waves. Some of the crew laughed at me but the Master Gunner, Thomas, told me it would pass and I would be alright after a few days. He is the only one who has been kind to me. The First Mate made me drink water every day even though I was sick again soon after. I have had nothing to eat until today when my uncle gave me a hard biscuit which he made me eat, even though I didn't want to. He didn't even ask how I was feeling. No one told me it would be like this. I hope we reach land soon!

**September 12**
Today I was made to work, even though I was still feeling sick. Harper, the First Mate, took my sack away, made me empty the bucket and told me to start washing down the deck with sea water and a brush. Uncle Edward wasn't on deck at the time so I couldn't tell him I wasn't well enough to work. I felt very weak but I did the job.

One of the men who does the cooking brought me some salt pork and ale when I had finished but it made me feel sick again so I gave it back to him and had a biscuit with some water. Thomas gave me his biscuit to eat too and sat by me to eat his own dinner. He didn't say much, but I felt better with him there.

We had hardly finished eating when the sails seemed to flap and strain at their ties. Everyone seemed to jump up and Harper fired orders to the rest of the crew to lower the sails. Thomas told me later that the wind had changed direction and it would have torn the sails.

Uncle Edward was suddenly there at the helm, steering the ship and giving orders sharply to the Mate, who in turn shouted at the men. Some of the crew were climbing the rigging to take down the big sails in the middle of the ship. Before I knew what was happening, the Mate was dragging me to my feet and shouting at me to climb up to the top of the mainmast with another man. We had to untie the ropes that held the small sail at the top. It was so high and the ship was tossing about in the water so that the mast seemed to lurch from side to side.

I don't know how I got to the top or how I managed to untie the sail ropes but I did. The other man kept shouting to me to tell me what to do. He kept me steady while I loosened the ropes, otherwise I am sure I would have fallen to the deck. I don't remember climbing down but I must have because I found myself sitting with my back pressed against the mast, huddled and shaking. The men just moved around me as if I wasn't there.

Eventually, Thomas came over and put a sack across my shoulders to

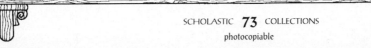

keep me warm but he didn't say anything. I know I shall never be able to go up on that rigging again, never!

**September 13**

I slept with the other men below deck last night. They each have their own bundle of sacking and their place on the wooden under-deck. They keep their belongings in small chests and roll up their bedding each morning. It is very cramped and smelly. Nobody seems to wash or change their clothes. Some of the crew have to stay awake through part of the night and they sleep during the day. Thomas told me that Uncle Edward shares the night watches with the First Mate and the Boatswain. I'm glad I don't have to do the night watch.

When we went up on deck this morning, we found that the wind had dropped during the night. I had to climb back up the rigging to help put up the sails. Thomas helped me, for although he is really a Gunner and looks after the four cannon, he does other sailing jobs, like everyone else in the crew. He told me that I have to go to the top because I am small and can balance better than a man on the small spars and ropes. He showed me how to pull up the sail and tie it tightly without losing my balance. He is so sure-footed because he has been sailing all his life. He started just like me, as a Ship's Boy.

My hands are raw and cut with the handling of the ropes. Thomas told me to soak them in salt water to harden them but it stung so much I nearly cried.

This afternoon I was sent to help the cook gut the fish and boil it! It's not fair! I might just as well be back at Plymouth working in the kitchen. I'll never get to be a Ship's Master if all I do is wash down the decks and cook!

**September 14**

We anchored in Calais harbour this afternoon. I helped unload the bales of wool on to the quayside. Uncle Edward went to get paid for delivering the wool and to see about picking up some more goods to take back to England. Before he went off he told me I could go ashore with Thomas and he gave me a penny from my pay to spend in the market.

It felt really strange to walk on land again. It seemed to pitch and roll as if we were still at sea and Thomas had to keep holding me steady. He said it always happened like that after being at sea for a few days. It wore off by the time we got to the market.

I couldn't understand what the people in the market were saying but I managed to buy some bread and cheese to eat. When we got back, we ate our food on deck in the dark. It was wonderful to eat soft bread again instead of those hard biscuits. I forced down some ale. We are each allowed one gallon a day but I can't possibly drink that much.

Thomas is fast asleep near by and my uncle is in his cabin on deck. I know now what Uncle Edward meant when he said it was hard at sea and it has been very difficult for me. I wondered today if I really did want to be a seaman but I know I do, even if it means doing all the messy jobs for years. I'm going to stick at it and show my uncle that he was right to take me on.

*Gill Goddard*

# VICTORIANS

## Twopence a tub

In 1848, miners from a small pit in the Black Country went on strike, protesting against their very low wages. The strike failed. No miners' strike succeeded until 1972.

The Manager dropped some fish on to the china plate he held, added an omelette and some breast of chicken, and passed the plate to his wife, who was seated at the table. For his own breakfast he chose bacon, eggs, a pair of kidneys and – after some humming – broiled chicken. He took his seat opposite his wife. He preferred private meals like this to be informal.

'Most of them *already* earn ten shillings a week, and yet they have the audacity to ask for *twopence* a tub.'

His wife smiled pleasantly. She was very pleasant.

'Twopence a tub would make their weekly wage a pound. Can you imagine! They would spend it all in drink, and the streets wouldn't be safe. We have already seen what happened in France – the King beheaded, the Queen too, the rabble ruling...'

'Oh, such a long time ago,' his wife said, in slight protest.

'That is the purpose of History, my dear – to warn. We have our warning. Twopence a tub!'

Around them, reflected in the dark, polished wood of the table, were little cut-glass dishes, glinting in the sunshine from the window: filled with fresh strawberries and preserves; and cream. Delicate glass plates, catching the light and holding it, were arranged with fingers of bread and butter; soft bread rolls. A stand of boiled eggs; a muffin dish full of buttered toast.

'Never mind,' the Manager went on, more calmly, wiping his mouth before drinking. 'I'll soon have them back at work. I sacked their leader. That will make them think twice before causing any more trouble. They'll soon be very glad to return to work.'

The dark, polished sideboard was covered with a harshly white cloth. On it were laid the silver-plated knives, forks, spoons; the translucent china and the china plates, painted with fine sprays of flowers and rose petals. And the tongue, the ham, and the cold veal pies.

'Really,' said the Manager, 'they have a wage perfectly sufficient to feed and clothe a small family, and yet they think nothing, nothing, of eleven children. Surely it must be obvious to the stupidest of them that you do not have more children than you can afford to keep.' He spoke with a little spit of jealousy. He had no children and he could afford to keep them... three pretty daughters and a son. 'But there – they have eleven children, find they cannot keep them and demand more wages. They should count their blessings and be thankful for what they have.' He poured himself another cup of coffee, added cream and sugar. 'My dear, do you think that the cook could produce one of those iced, cream gateaux for tonight? I feel that I deserve a treat.'

The polished side-table held the hot food. Poached eggs, grilled bacon, dressed fish, kidneys, lamb cutlets, tender broiled chicken and a dish of ham-filled omelettes.

And when they had finished, the servants came in to clear the table and wash the dishes.

Susan Price

# Billy the nailer

Billy is eleven years old.

Billy makes nails

He lives and works in a squalid cottage, not much bigger than a stable, along with his family of nailers. Hetty and Lily, his sisters, work too. When Billy manages to make a thousand nails a day he will be a fully-skilled nailmaker. Hetty can make a thousand nails a day, but Hetty is older than Billy and has been working longer. When Billy and Hetty and Lily can make one thousand, two hundred nails they will get five pennies and three farthings for those nails.

The hammers they use are heavy, for children anyway. They weigh one and a quarter pounds. It takes twelve blows from the hammer to make one nail. If you work it out, it means that Billy, Hetty and Lily have to lift eighteen thousand pounds in hammerweight to earn their five pennies and three farthings. You would think they are strong children, lifting and hammering all that weight, day after day, morning till night. But they are not. They're small, puny for their age. In a twelve hour working day their lunch is only bread with perhaps a bit of 'tainted' meat – meat that others, more fortunate than they, wouldn't touch.

None of them can read, or write. Taken out of school before they are ten and set to work to help to feed the big family, they haven't learned much. Maybe they can write their names. Nailmaking is the only work in their area. Everyone exists by nailing. And school fees are threepence a week. You don't learn much for threepence a week. And your clothes, or rags, mean you can't really go to Sunday school either, like respectable children.

What does Billy think of his life? If you ask him he doesn't complain. Of the heat from the forge's fire, the noise of the hammers. Or that he has no shoes. Or that he is beaten, often, hard.

And if you ask him, after a long day striving for five pennies and three farthings, whether he is tired, he probably wouldn't even know what you meant.

Billy is a nailmaker.

That's all he know.

Ann Bonner

# A seamstress's story

Once upon a time I lived in the country.

I say 'once upon a time'! It may have been only two, or three years since, but I have lost count of the years, the months, the days and long, long hours that I have been slave to my mistress and to this needle I hold. My childhood (till I was fourteen), with my poor mother and father, my sisters and my brothers, is locked away in some small corner of my mind as if it never was. Only in dreams do I sometimes find it again.

This garret is our prison. Here we work, eat and sleep, the other seamstresses and I. Far below us is the street, where the ladies of high fashion, our customers, ride in carriages, and the dandy wears his shirt of fancy frills. We are paid sixpence for one of those shirts. It takes us eighteen hours to make it.

In the busy season we rise from our mattresses at five and work till midnight, or later. In winter when our garret room is cold and blind fog stalks the streets of London we stitch fine stuffs of velvet and warm wool. In summer the needle eye of the sun burns its rays across the roof. We sweat while stitching cool cotton, soft sweet silk.

Our fingers, though nimble, grow weary with stitching. Our shoulders hunched. Our backs no longer straight, but locked into a curve from bending at our work.

By lamplight we stitch a fine seam. By lamplight our eyes grow dim, begin to water, swell. We stitch on. At the end of the week there will be half a crown.

I sleep next to Mary, Rose, and Eliza.

The garret is stuffy, crowded with sleepers sleeping as though they were dead. I fancy, for a moment, that I can smell hay new-cut on a June breeze. The memory penetrates the foul air, and I am able to breathe again. Then sleep myself.

Till tomorrow.

When I pick up my needle and thread.

Ann Bonner

# The chimney boy's song

Inside the chimney, high I climb.
It's dark inside the sooty stack.
I bang my head, I graze my back,
I lose all sense of passing time.
Inside the chimney, high I climb.

Inside the chimney, high I climb.
Far, far above... a patch of blue
where one white cloud drifts into view.
I stop to rest, but that's a crime.
Inside the chimney, high I climb.

Inside the chimney, high I climb.
My bare feet slip on crumbling bricks.
I clear rooks' nests – dead leaves and sticks.
The Master yells, 'get working, brat!'
I'm starved. Sometimes I eat stewed rat.
Soot's in my hair. I'm licking grime.
Inside the chimney, high I climb.

Wes Magee

# The little chimney sweep

Once upon a time there was a little chimney-sweep, and his name was Tom. He lived in a great town in the North country, where there were plenty of chimneys to sweep, and plenty of money for Tom to earn and his master to spend. He could not read nor write, and did not care to do either; and he never washed himself, for there was no water up the court where he lived. He had never been taught to say his prayers. He cried half his time, and laughed the other half. He cried when he had to climb the dark flues, rubbing his poor knees and elbows raw; and when the soot got into his eyes, which it did every day in the week; and when his master beat him, which he did every day in the week, and when he had not enough to eat, which happened every day in the week likewise. And he laughed the other half of the day, when he was tossing halfpennies with the other boys, or playing leap-frog over the posts, or bowling stones at the horses' legs as they trotted by, which last was excellent fun, when there was a wall at hand behind which to hide. As for chimney-sweeping, and being hungry, and being beaten, he took all that for the way of the world, like the rain and snow and thunder, and stood manfully with his back to it till it was over, as his old donkey did to a hailstorm; and then shook his ears and was as jolly as ever; and thought of the fine times coming, when he would be a man, and a master sweep, and sit in the public-house with a quart of beer and a long pipe, and play cards for silver money, and wear velveteens, and ankle-jacks, and keep a white

bulldog with one grey ear, and carry her puppies in his pocket, just like a man. And he would have apprentices, one, two, three, if he could. How he would bully them, and knock them about, just as his master did to him; and make them carry home the soot sacks, while he rode before them on his donkey with a pipe in his mouth and a flower in his buttonhole, like a king at the head of his army. Yes, there were good times coming; and, when his master let him have a pull at the leavings of his beer, Tom was the jolliest boy in the whole town.

From The Water Babies by Charles Kingsley

# Child

Child of the past
sits in the mine
chilly and dark.

Child of the present
plays in the sunlight
out in the park.

Child of the past
clambers the chimney
grimy with soot.

Child of the present
slithers with glee
down the water chute.

Child of the past
sleeps in the doorway,
stone for a bed.

Child of the present
snuggles a pillow
under her sleeping head.

Child of the past
living in darkness,
hungry, empty of love.

Child of the present
out in the sunlight,
laughing, blue sky above.

Tony Mitton

# The Watercress Seller

Now all aloud the wind and rain
Beat sharp upon the window pane,
   And though 'tis hardly light,
   I hear that little girl go by,
   Who does 'Fine watercresses' cry,
   Morning, and noon, and night.

I saw her pass by yesterday,
The snow upon the pavement lay,
   Her hair was white with sleet;
   She shook with cold, as she did cry,
   'Fine watercresses, come and buy,'
   And naked were her feet.

And with one hand, so red and cold,
She did her tattered bonnet hold,
   The other held her shawl,
Which was too thin to keep her warm,
   But naked left each little arm,
   It was so very small.

Her watercresses froze together,
Yet she, through the cold, bitter weather,
   Went on from street to street:
   And thus she goes out every day,
   For she can earn no other way
   The bread which she doth eat.

Thomas Miller

# The Lamplighter

My tea is nearly ready and the sun has left the sky;
It's time to take the window to see Leerie going by;
For every night at teatime and before you take your seat,
With lantern and with ladder he comes posting up the street.

Now Tom would be a driver and Maria go to sea,
And my papa's a banker and as rich as he can be;
But I, when I am stronger and can choose what I'm to do,
O Leerie, I'll go round at night and light the lamps with you!

For we are very lucky, with a lamp before the door,
And Leerie stops to light it as he lights so many more;
And O! before you hurry by with ladder and with light,
O Leerie, see a little child and nod to him tonight!

Robert Louis Stevenson

# '...the terrible laws the English government has made against us...'

In the year 1854, the tenants of the small farms of Greenyards were being brutally
evicted so that the land could be sold at enormous profit for sheep grazing.
In this extract from A Pistol in Greenyards by Mollie Hunter, the tenants are
addressed by Donald Ban, grandfather of 15-year-old Connal who relates the story.

My grandfather stepped forward, holding himself so erect for all his sixty-eight years, that the men around him looked small beside his great height. Donald Ban – Donald of the fair hair, they had named him in his youth, but now his hair, which he wore flowing on to his shoulders in the old style, was white. And with this and the long white beard of him, he looked like a prophet out of the Old Testament. Like a prophet too, he spoke in a loud, ringing voice of the death and doom and destruction that had followed the coming of the sheep to the Highlands.

'There is no need to tell my own generation or my sons' generation of this,' he cried, 'for they have seen it all with their own eyes! It is our grandsons and grand-daughters – you young people there who are not yet twenty years of age and so are too young to have seen an eviction, who must realize how things will be if we allow this to happen to us. Understand now, my children, if we are driven from this glen there will be nowhere for us to go but beyond the seas! The sheep-walks are all round us now. Our little glen is one of the last where people have been allowed to live in the old way and so there is no other land for us.

Homeless, because our houses will be burned by the Sheriff's men, landless because we will be driven out of our farms, we will suffer the fate that thousands of Highlanders have already suffered. Starvation or exile will be our choice!

'The cities of the south have nothing to offer us for we have no skill in city crafts – and even those of you who could reach a city and find employment there would find yourself suffocating in the smoke and dirt of its filthy air. You might manage to survive such a life, but even if you did – you young people who have been brought up in the admonition of the Lord to respect your parents and to care for the sick and the aged – you could do so only at the expense of the helpless ones you would leave behind you.'

So still were the people listening to him that there was not even the sound of grass or heather-stems rustling underfoot. It seemed to me that we were held to him by some invisible bond and, as if he sensed the pull of it between us, my grandfather gave a tug on it then that sent shivers running up my back.

'It is more than our homes they would take from us,' he cried. 'It is the heritage to which we have been born and which has been ours for generation upon generation, so that now it is only in the high, pure air of mountains that our spirits can breathe! Out of sight of them we would sicken and die with longing for the feel of heather under our feet, for the sight of bracken glinting in the sun, and for the sound of rivers rushing down between the stones! We old people would sicken and die, and even you young people would never cease to feel the ache of longing in your hearts, for the tall mountains and the green valleys between them are as much home to the Highlander as is the roof over his head. I, Donald Ban, who have wandered the world over soldiering in many countries, do tell you this now. If you leave Greenyards you will wake many a night, weeping. And wondering why there should be such a fierce ache of pain in your hearts will know such bitterness of sorrow as comes only to those who have been driven forth, never to return, from the glen of their fathers.'

The great roll of this voice ceased. There was a moment's silence that was broken by a voice crying, 'It is true! Donald Ban has spoken the bitter truth!' then they all pressed forward on him shouting that they would die rather than leave the glen. Some wept, and some were so moved by his words that they seized his hand and kissed it.

'We will not go, Donald Ban! We will not go! No one shall drive us from our home!'

The cailleachs beside me were babbling of other evictions; of Strathnaver, where they had not waited till the people were out before they fired the houses so that old people and children had been caught in the flames; of Glencalvie, where the only shelter the people could find on the stormy night of their eviction was the lee of the churchyard wall.

I said nothing and I did not move. I could not, for the life of me, for the knowledge was on me stronger than it had ever been before that my feet were on the soil which had been trodden by those of my blood for five hundred years. My feet were rooted to it, it seemed to me then, as deeply as the heather that grew there. And in the wonder and pride of that moment, I was speechless.

'They came early this morning – men with dogs and guns and torches. There were drovers with them, Englishmen and Lowlanders with loud voices and money jingling in their pockets. The cattle were auctioned off to them. The men with the torches set fire to the houses while the bidding went on. They levered off the roof-beams with crow-bars to make the wood burn faster.'

'Were any of the people hurt?' I asked anxiously, and in the same flat voice Katrine said:

'Some were – the sick, the elderly and the very young. Those who could not get quickly enough away from the flames. They suffered burns, and bruises from falling beams. And some of the women who were seized by a kind of madness that would not let them believe they were losing their homes had to be dragged out by the wreckers. They were not gently handled.'

'But there were no more deaths?'

'Old Phemy Munro – you know, Hugh's widow – I think she will die by nightfall.'

The steady toneless flow of Katrine's speech faltered and for the first time she looked directly at me.

'They would not give our men time to carry the poor crippled creature out in a blanket as they begged to be allowed to do. They slung her out in the snow like a heap of old clothes.'

**Cailleachs** - *old women*

From A Pistol in Greenyards by Mollie Hunter

# The workhouse

Jim Jarvis, his mother and his two sisters, Emily and Lizzie, are all homeless. His mother's friend Rosie has agreed to look after the two girls, but Jim and his mother have nowhere to go. Jim's mother is also desperately ill and when she collapses in the street they are taken to the dreaded workhouse. The next morning Jim learns that his mother is dead. His new home is presided over by a cruel couple called Mr and Mrs Sissons and he learns about the workhouse from a bent-backed man called Joseph.

Jim forced his fists deep in his pockets and turned his face away. There were boys all round him, shuffling out to the cold yard, and they blurred into smudges of grey. He screwed up his eyes against the terrible blinding white of the sky. He wouldn't cry here. His lungs were bursting and he thought he would never be able to gasp for air again, but he couldn't cry here. The only person he wanted to be with was Rosie. She would know what to do. She would tell Emily and Lizzie. But there was no chance of being with Rosie.

'I want to go home,' he said.

Joseph swung his head and spat. 'Home?' he said. 'What d'you mean, home? What's this, if it ain't home?'

So, Jim thought, this is my home now, this huge building with iron bars at the window and iron railings outside. His parents must be Mr and Mrs Sissons, as thin and waxy-pale as candles. And if they were his parents then his brother and sisters were the shambling, skinny boys who slept and sobbed in the same room as him, and the scrawny girls who seemed to have forgotten how to smile.

'Can't I see her, all the same?'

Joseph shook his head. 'She was took into the dead-house in the night, and put on the paupers' cart before light, son. Speedy despatch, paupers get. No money for bells nor nothing like that, eh?'

Jim went dumbly from room to room as he was told, from the sleeping-boxes to the yard, the refectory, the yard, and back to his box ... It was like a slow dance, and the steps were always the same, repeated day after day after day.

Morning started with the six o'clock bell, when all the boys had to wash under the pump. Joseph watched them, swinging his head from side to side and bending his neck round like a hunched bird of prey. He kept flapping his arms across his bent chest to beat the cold away.

'Get yerselfs washed quick, boys,' he said. 'Afore the wevver bites me bones off.'

Across the yard from the pump was the asylum. Mad people were locked up. They wailed and shrieked for hours on end. They stretched their hands out through the bars of their prison. 'Give us some bread, boy!' they begged. 'Let me out! Let me out!'

'Don't take no notice of them,' a woolly-headed boy whispered to him one day. 'They're mad. They're animals.' Jim was shocked. He stared again at the men and women and children who were all squashed up together. Their cage was too small to hold them all. Their wailings echoed round the yard all the time. 'Animals, animals,' Jim said to himself, trying to drive their noises out of his head. He looked away from them, pretending they weren't there.

'No, they're not animals, Jim,' Joseph told him. 'They're people, they are. People, Jim. My ma's in there.'

There was a shed at the other end of the yard. Boys gazed out at them through a small barred window. Their white faces were even more frightening than the wailings of the mad people. Joseph sidled over to Jim that first morning and swung his arm across the boy's shoulder, bringing his head round to mutter down Jim's ear. 'Now, them's the boys what tried to run away. They catch 'em and beat 'em and stick 'em in there till they're good. Remember that.'

After the cold wash in the yard Jim had to help to clean it out with brooms twice as tall as he was. They had to sweep it till the ground was bare and clean, even if hundreds of leaves had fallen in the night and come drifting over the high walls. At breakfast the boys queued up with their bowls in their hands for bread and tea. The bread was meant to last for every meal, but if Jim tried to save it he soon had it stolen by one of the older boys. He learnt to gulp his food down as quickly as they did; boiled meat at dinner time, cheese at night, all swallowed rapidly and in silence.

Sometimes Mr Sissons read to them while they were eating, always Bible stories, and his whistly voice would glide round the echoing room over the clatter of knives and forks. Jim never listened to him. All he wanted to do was to think about his mother and Emily and Lizzie.

But every now and then Mr Sissons stopped reading and lowered his book. He stared round the room, his eyes like round, glassy balls and his fingers cracking together. Jim stopped eating, afraid that he had done something wrong. He sat with his spoon held somewhere between his mouth and his bowl, until the boy next to him nudged him into action again. Mr Sissons put down his book and jumped off his dais. He came gliding down the aisles between the long tables like a thin black shadow. Jim could just see him out of the corner of his eye. He daren't for the life of him look up.

The master lunged out at one of the boys at random, pulling him away from his bench by the back of his collar and sending his bowl flying and the contents spattering across the faces and clothes of the other boys.

'Misbehaving, were you?' he said, his voice as dry as a hissing swan's. 'Eating like a pig? Get to the trough, animal!' And the boy crouched on his hands and knees in front of a pig's trough that was always there, and had to eat his food from that, without a fork or spoon. Sometimes there were half a dozen people troughing, usually just for Mr Sisson's amusement.

'Please don't let it be me. Please don't let it be me,' Jim said deep inside himself as Mr Sissons glided past and the air turned as cold as ice around him.

Jim had no idea how long he had been at the workhouse when he first thought of trying to escape. At first it seemed an impossible idea, as impossible as making the pump in the yard turn into a tree and blaze out with leaves and blossoms. He remembered the runaway boys locked up in the shed in the yard for everyone to see. Even so, he had to try. One day, he promised himself, he would go. He would watch out every moment, sharp as a bird, for a chance to fly. And when he did he would never be caught.

He was almost too afraid to allow himself to think about it, in case Mr Sissons pounced inside his thoughts and strapped him to a chair and beat him as he beat other reckless boys.

*From Street Child by Berlie Doherty*

# A Victorian school

The child looked round the room as she took her seat. There were a couple of forms (benches), notched and cut and inked all over; a small desk perched on four legs, at which no doubt the master sat; a few dog's-eared books upon a high shelf; and beside them a motley collection of peg-tops, balls, kites, fishing-lines, marbles, half-eaten apples, and other confiscated property of idle urchins.

Displayed on hooks upon the wall in all their terrors were the cane and ruler; and near them, on a shelf of its own, the dunce's cap, made of old newspapers and decorated with glaring wafers of the largest size. But, the great ornaments of the walls were certain moral sentences fairly copied in good round text and well-worked sums in simple addition and multiplication.

*From The Old Curiosity Shop by Charles Dickens.*

# School

School began at nine o'clock, but the hamlet children set out on their mile-and-a-half walk there as soon as possible after their seven o'clock breakfast, partly because they liked plenty of time to play on the road and partly because their mothers wanted them out of the way before house-cleaning began.

Up the long, straight road they straggled, in twos and threes and in gangs, their flat, rush dinner-baskets over their shoulders and their shabby little coats on their arms against rain. In cold weather some of them carried two hot potatoes which had been in the oven, or in the ashes, all night, to warm their hands on the way and to serve as a light lunch on arrival.

They were strong, lusty children, let loose from control, and there was plenty of shouting, quarrelling, and often fighting among them. In more peaceful moments they would squat in the dust of the road and play marbles, or sit on a stone heap and play dibs with pebbles, or climb into the hedges after birds' nests or blackberries, or to pull long trails of bryony to wreathe round their hats. In winter they would slide on the ice on the puddles, or make snowballs – soft ones for their friends, and hard ones with a stone inside for their enemies.

After the first mile or so the dinner-baskets would be raided; or they would creep through the bars of the padlocked field gates for turnips to pare with the teeth and munch, or for handfuls of green pea shucks, or ears of wheat, to rub out the sweet, milky grain between the hands and devour. In spring they ate the young green from the hawthorn hedges, which they called 'bread and cheese', and sorrel leaves from the wayside, which they called 'sour grass', and in autumn there was an abundance of haws and blackberries and sloes and crab-apples for them to feast upon. There was always something to eat, and they ate, not so much because they were hungry as from habit and relish of the wild food.

At that early hour there was little traffic upon the road. Sometimes, in winter, the children would hear the pounding of galloping hoofs and a string of hunters, blanketed up to the ears and ridden and led by grooms, would loom up out of the mist and thunder past on the grass verges. At other times the steady tramp and jingle of the teams going afield would approach, and, as they passed, fathers would pretend to flick their offspring with whips, saying. 'There! that's for that time you deserved it an' didn't get it'; while elder brothers, themselves at school only a few months before, would look patronizingly down from the horses' backs and call: 'Get out o' th' way, you kids!'

A favourite amusement with these was to fall in a body upon some unoffending companion, usually a small girl in a clean frock, and to 'run her', as they called it. This meant chasing her until they caught her, then dragging her down and sitting upon her, tearing her clothes, smudging her face, and tousling her hair in the process. She might scream and cry and say she would 'tell on' them; they took no notice until, tiring of the sport, they would run whooping off, leaving her sobbing and exhausted.

The persecuted one never 'told on' them, even when reproved by the schoolmistress for her dishevelled condition, for she knew that, if she had, there would have been a worse 'running' to endure on the way home, and one that went to the tune of:

Tell-tale tit!
Cut her tongue a-slit,
And every little puppy-dog shall have a little bit!

It was no good telling the mothers either, for it was the rule of the hamlet never to interfere in the children's quarrels. 'Let 'em fight it out among theirselves,' the woman would say; and if a child complained the only response would be: 'You must've been doin' summat to them. If you'd've left them alone, they'd've left you alone; so don't come bringing your tales home to me!' It was harsh schooling; but the majority seemed to thrive upon it, and the few quieter and more sensitive children soon learned either to start early and get to school first, or to linger behind, dipping under bushes and lurking inside field gates until the main body had passed.

From Lark Rise to Candleford by Flora Thompson

# Victorian school rhymes

You will never be sorry
For using gentle words,
For doing your best,
For being kind to the poor,
For looking before leaping,
For thinking before speaking,
For doing what you can to make others happy.

Anonymous

Why do drill?
Children who do drill,
Seldom are ill,
Seldom look pale,
Delicate and frail,
Seldom are sulky and
Seldom are spiteful
But always delightful.
So dears, I still
Beg you to drill

Jennet Humphrey, Laugh and Learn, 1890

Marching rhyme
We march to our places,
With clean hands and faces,
And pay great attention
to all we are told.
For we know we shall never
be happy and clever,
But learning is better
than silver and gold.

Anonymous

A child's morning prayer
I thank thee, Lord, for the quiet rest,
and for the care of me,
Oh let me through the day be blest,
and kept from harm by thee,
Help me to please my parents dear,
and do whatever they tell;
Bless all my friends, both far and near,
and keep them safe and well.

Anonymous

# A Victorian schoolmaster

This journal shows that not all Victorian schools were places of cruelty. Even though the schoolmaster is attacked by one of his pupils, he tries a number of milder punishments to try to bring the boy back into line.

### 7th September

I was called into the lower school this morning to deal with John Bailey aged 5 who had bitten his teacher, taking a piece out of her hand. He did this because he was told to stay in and read, he having during the reading lesson thrown the book across the room in a temper.

The boy tried to bite my cane in halves and then made an effort to get my hand between his teeth. I put him in the corner and he commenced to kick the cupboard and the nearby children.

I tried to restrain him with a hand on his shoulder but in his mad passion to free himself the blouse tore.

There was little alternative but to place him in the playground, whereupon he threw himself upon the door and bit the iron padlock.

A man working in one of the nearby gardens told the boy's father that we were ill-treating his child.

Mr Bailey collected his son and left but not before using the most insulting language against myself and the Staff. He has threatened to summons me.

### 10th September

The child John Bailey has returned to the school today and seems sorry for his conduct, promising better behaviour in the future. Later in the day I had to reprimand him for throwing slates across the room whereupon he tore at my hand with his finger nails in a most savage manner – kicking furiously at my legs and screaming at the top of his voice. As the father declined a request by one of my pupil teachers to remove the child I was forced once again to place him forcibly in the playground – he threw stones and dirt through the window.

I informed Mr Thomson, a school Manager, that the child constituted a very serious danger to the school. A letter will be sent to Mr Bailey informing him that his son's foul language and disgraceful conduct renders it quite impossible that he should remain at the school.

It is my great wish that this concludes a very disturbing episode. I was grateful for the positive support of the Managers.

From The Journal of a Victorian Schoolmaster in Dorset 1863-64, compiled by Barry Wheeler

# Harvest Home

After the mowing and reaping and binding came the carrying, the busiest time of all. Every man and boy put his best foot forward then, for, when the corn was cut and dried it was imperative to get it stacked and thatched before the weather broke. All day and far into the twilight the yellow-and-blue painted farm wagons passed and repassed along the roads between the field and the stack-yard. Big cart-horses returning with an empty wagon were made to gallop like two-year-olds. Straws hung on the roadside hedges and many a gate-post was knocked down through hasty driving. In the fields men pitch-forked the sheaves to the one who was building the load on the wagon, and the air resounded with *Hold tights* and *Wert ups* and *Who-o-oas*. The *Hold tight!* was no empty cry; sometimes, in the past, the man on top of the load had not held tight or not tight enough. There were tales of fathers and grandfathers whose necks or backs had been broken by a fall from a load, and of other fatal accidents afield, bad cuts from scythes, pitchforks passing through feet, to be followed by lockjaw, and of sunstroke; but, happily, nothing of this kind happened on that particular farm in the 'eighties.

At last, in the cool dusk of an August evening, the last load was brought in, with a nest of merry boys' faces among the sheaves on the top, and the men walking alongside with pitchforks on shoulders. As they passed along the roads they shouted:

Harvest home! Harvest home!
Merry, merry, merry harvest home!

and women came to their cottage gates and waved, and the few passers-by looked up and smiled their congratulations. The joy and pleasure of the labourers in their task well done was pathetic, considering their very small share in the gain. But it was genuine enough; for they still loved the soil, and rejoiced in their own work and skill in bringing forth the fruits of the soil and harvest home put the crown on their year's work.

As they approached the farm-house their song changed to:

Harvest home! Harvest home!
Merry, merry, merry harvest home!
Our bottles are empty, our barrels won't run,
And we think it's a very dry harvest home.

and the farmer came out, followed by his daughters and maids with jugs and bottles and mugs, and drinks were handed round amidst general congratulations. Then the farmer invited the men to his harvest home dinner, to be held in a few days' time, and the adult workers dispersed to add up their harvest money and to rest their weary bones. The boys and youths, who could never have too much of a good thing, spent the rest of the evening circling the hamlet and shouting 'Merry, merry, merry harvest home!' until the stars came out and at last silence fell upon the fat rickyard and the stripped fields.

*From Lark Rise to Candleford by Flora Thompson*

# The charge of the Light Brigade

Half a league, half a league,
Half a league onward,
All in the valley of Death
Rode the six hundred.
'Forward, the Light Brigade!
Charge for the guns!' he said:
Into the valley of Death
Rode the six hundred.

'Forward, the Light Brigade!'
Was there a man dismay'd?
Not tho' the soldier knew
Some one had blunder'd:
Their's not to make reply,
Their's not to reason why,
Their's but to do and die:
Into the valley of Death
Rode the six hundred.

Cannon to right of them,
Cannon to left of them,
Cannon in front of them
Volley'd and thunder'd;
Storm'd at with shot and shell,
Boldly they rode and well,
Into the jaws of Death,
Into the mouth of Hell
Rode the six hundred.

Flash'd all their sabres bare,
Flash'd as they turn'd in air
Sabring the gunners there,
Charging an army, while
All the world wonder'd:
Plunged in the battery-smoke
Right thro' the line they broke;
Cossack and Russian
Reel'd from the sabre-stroke
Shatter'd and sunder'd.
Then they rode back, but not
Not the six hundred.
Cannon to right of them,
Cannon to left of them;
Cannon behind them
Volley'd and thunder'd;
Storm'd at with shot and shell,
While horse and hero fell,
They that had fought so well
Came thro' the jaws of Death,
Back from the mouth of Hell,
All that was left of them.
Left of six hundred.

When can their glory fade?
O the wild charge they made!
All the world wonder'd.
Honour the charge they made!
Honour the Light Brigade,
Noble six hundred!

Alfred, Lord Tennyson

# Having a lovely time: bathing and bathing machines

30th July 1847: 'Drove down to the beach with my maid and went into the bathing machine, where I undressed and bathed in the sea (for the first time in my life), a very nice bathing woman attending me. I thought it delightful until I put my head under the water, when I thought I should be stifled.' So wrote Her Majesty Queen Victoria in her diary.

By the middle of the nineteenth century, seaside resorts were becoming places for enjoyment whereas previously they had been visited by people who believed that 'taking the waters' would do them good.

Almost one hundred years before Queen Victoria's first dip in the sea, Dr Richard Russell had written a book in which he declared that sea bathing and the drinking of sea water could cure such diseases as scurvy, jaundice and gout. It became fashionable to drink up to a litre of warm sea water before bathing.

Much bathing was done before dawn to ensure privacy, but the development of the bathing machine meant that people could bathe in private as and when they liked. The Thanet Guide of 1763 describes the bathing machine as having:

'Large wheels so that it could be pulled out by a horse into the sea and then turned round so that its double doors opened away from the shore beneath a large screen or umbrella which enclosed a private pool.'

At the back of the bathing houses were short flights of wooden steps down which the bathers went as the guide drove the machine up to the stage. The driver who sat on a moveable bench, admitted the bather and then drove out into the bay. A line that ran along the machine could raise or lower the umbrella.

The popularity of sea bathing grew rapidly:

'There is (says a writer in 1769) an epidemical disorder that was formerly quite unknown... which seizes whole families here in town (London) at this time of year. In a word, whatever the nature of the complaint may be, it is imagined that nothing will remove it but spending the summer months in some dirty fishing town near the seashore.'

By far the biggest boost for seaside resorts was the coming of the railways in the early part of Queen Victoria's reign. Previously people had travelled to the coast by coach, sailing ship or steamboat but the railways opened up the coast to everyone. More and more town dwellers took advantage of this development and found the time and money to travel far from home and to enjoy themselves.

Lewis Carroll, the writer of *Alice in Wonderland*, described what was taking place: 'When people get weary of life, they rush off to the seaside to see what bathing machines will do for them'.

By 1862, Margate had found it necessary to introduce certain regulations regarding the use of bathing machines:

That a distance of not less than 60 feet shall be preserved by the Owners and Drivers of Bathing Machines between the Bathing Machines from which Females are bathing and those from which Males are bathing.

That the Owner of every machine shall gratuitously provide for the use of Female bathers engaging such Machines, gowns or dresses; and for the use of Male bathers engaging such Machines, drawers, or such other suitable covering as will prevent indecent exposure of the person.

That no boat or vessel let to hire for the purpose of sailing or rowing for pleasure shall approach from the sea within the distance of two hundred yards of any Bathing Machine in actual use, except for the purpose of saving life or other strictly necessary purpose.

Many people resented being unable to bathe in the traditional manner and in 1874 the Rev Francis Kilvert wrote in his diary: 'At Shanklin one has to adopt the detestable custom of bathing in drawers.'

In 1901, Bexhill was the first resort to allow mixed bathing and other resorts soon followed. This new freedom meant the gradual disappearance of bathing machines on our beaches.

Brian Moses

# Preparing for Sunday

'Preparing for Sunday' appeared in a children's magazine in 1868.

Haste! Put your playthings all away,
Tomorrow is the Sabbath Day.
Come bring to me your Noah's Ark,
Your pretty tinkling music cart;
Because, my love, you must not play,
But holy keep the Sabbath Day.
Anonymous

# The Victorian music hall

Slingsby and his friend Edward are two young men who are out on the town in search of entertainment.

'Where to guv'nor;?'

'To the *King's*,' Slingsby replied and, with a crack of his whip and the jingle of gleaming harness, the hansom drew into the stream of traffic heading westwards. Not long afterwards it pulled up before the King's Music Hall, the two friends alighted and plunged into the mass of people struggling to enter the building. They showed their tickets – two shillings (10p) each for the stalls – and moved into an auditorium that was all crimson plush and gilded plaster. The place was already full and there was a warm aroma of cheap scent, cigar smoke, oranges... and people.

Hardly had they sat down than a roar of welcome announced the arrival of the chairman, who took his place at a table at one side of the stage. His duty was to introduce each act and to exchange pleasantries – and occasionally insults – with the audience.

The programme followed the usual pattern. A number of acrobats in tights threw themselves, and each other, about the stage; several ladies and gentlemen of varying ages and sizes came on and sang; comedians told funny stories before bursting into song themselves. One unusual item was an exhibition given by a young lady, who, when the curtain rose, was revealed standing beside a large tank of water. An elderly gentleman in evening dress explained each part of her act, telling the audience, as if no one could see what was happening, that she was gathering shells under water, opening and shutting her mouth, and performing other similar 'impossible' feats. Finally he announced, 'Ladies and gentlemen, she will now adopt the attitude of prayer,' whereupon the lady sank to her knees with folded hands and remained in that position for a while as the orchestra solemnly played 'The Maiden's Prayer'.

Finally, a little out of breath from her exertions, she rose sleek and dripping to the surface, hopped numbly out and bowed herself off. She had obviously made a hit with one part of the audience at least, for she was received with a torrent of applause from the people in the *gods*, the balcony above Edward's head.

An expectant hush then settled on the audience as the chairman rose, his hammer uplifted, to announce the star of the evening. 'Ladies and gentlemen,' he boomed, 'the King's Music Hall is proud, nay, exceeding proud, to present the great, the stupendous, the incomparable, the one and only ... *Dan Leno!*' and to applause that seemed to shake the whole building, a little man bounced onto the stage. He was the most famous comedian of his time and his sketches, songs and clog-dancing always 'brought the house down'. He ended his act, leaving the audience screaming for more, to dash out of the stage door into the waiting carriage and hurry to the next theatre, for in those days even the great 'stars' such as *Marie Lloyd, Little Tich, George Robey* and *Harry Tate* played at least four theatres a night.

The show ended with a group of black-faced 'Minstrels', a type of act that was already losing much of its former popularity. After the Minstrels had gone through their repertoire of 'My Old Kentucky Home', 'Poor Old Joe', 'The Camptown Races' and so on, a Union Jack was lowered from above and they concluded with a loyal and stirring song written especially about The Queen and her Jubilee. It was very much in key with the mood of the audience and they ended to great applause.

From One Day in Victorian England by Alastair Scott

# The Grace Darling Song

Grace Darling was born in Bamburgh in 1815. She lived on the Farne Islands, off the coast of Northumberland. Her father was keeper of the Longstone Lighthouse. On 7 September 1838, a paddle-steamer, the Forfarshire was wrecked in a storm. Many of the people on board had drowned, but some were clinging to a rock. In fierce seas, Grace helped her father to launch their small rowing boat and rescue the survivors. Nine people were saved and Grace became a national heroine. Artists arrived to paint her portrait, the national papers wrote of her daring deed and plays were performed about her exploit. Grace was bemused by such fame. Four years later she died of tuberculosis. This song is taken from a leaflet in the Grace Darling Museum, Bamburgh, Northumberland.

T'was on the Longstone Lighthouse,
There dwelt an English maid;
Pure as the air around her,
Of danger ne'er afraid.
One morning just at daybreak,
A storm tossed wreck she spied:
And tho' to try seemed madness,
'I'll save the crew!' she cried.

CHORUS
And she pulled away, o'er the rolling sea,
Over the waters blue.
'Help! Help!' she could hear the cry
of the shipwrecked crew.
But Grace had an English heart,
And the raging storm she braved;
She pulled away mid the dashing spray,
And the crew she saved.

They to the rocks were clinging,
A crew of nine all told;
Between them and the lighthouse,
The sea like mountains rolled.
Said Grace, 'Come help me father
We'll launch that boat,' said she.
Her father cried: 'T'is madness,
To face that raging sea!'

CHORUS

One murmered prayer 'Heaven guard us!'
And then they were afloat;
Between them and destruction,
The planks of that frail boat.
Then spoke the maiden's father:
'Return or doomed are we.'
But up spoke brave Grace Darling:
'Alone I'll brave the sea.'

CHORUS

They bravely rode the billows,
And reached the rock at length:
They saved the storm tossed sailors,
In Heaven alone their strength.
Go, tell the wide world over
What English pluck can do;
And sing of brave Grace Darling,
Who nobly saved the crew.

Anonymous

# The last night of Jubilee Week

Daisy Simpkins is a housemaid in a London town house. She walks through the streets of London on the last night of Queen Victoria's Jubilee Week in 1887.

When her young brothers and sisters had been put to bed, with a neighbour to sit with them, Daisy went out with her mother and father to stroll around and enjoy the last night of Jubilee Week. Although it was past 10 pm., there were crowds of people in the streets, all in a happy and festive mood.

Feeling very grown-up, Daisy walked along, thoroughly enjoying the sights and scenes around her. This was the life she really enjoyed – brash, noisy and genuine – and a world apart from the quiet dignity of Mount Street and Mayfair.

At one corner a small crowd was watching a group of black-faced minstrels playing outside a public house; at another, a smaller group was watching a man and a woman arguing at the tops of their voices. Here and there, clusters of women, with bare arms and with shawls around their shoulders, stood and gossiped with one another.

The three walked along into Hammersmith Broadway and then west along King Street. This was the great market street of West London with tram-lines down the centre of a street which was lined with *costers'* barrows and kerb-stone sellers. Here were the greatest crowds of all, men, women and children, loitering at the barrows and looking into the gas-lamp lit shop windows. By now, however, some of the stalls were beginning to close and there were bargains to be had.

From time to time a sudden shaft of light would flood onto the crowded pavements as the door of a public house was flung open and a cheerful customer, frequently singing, would stagger out into the night. No doubt many on the morrow would hold their aching heads and regret the money that had been recklessly squandered on drink. No doubt, also, the night out would result in a visit to the pawnshop on the Monday morning. Pawnshops – London and the major cities were full of them – played an important part in the lives of the poor. It was a common sight to see a number of children, the weekly bundle on their laps, waiting outside pawnshops for them to open on a Monday morning. Many families pawned their Sunday clothes regularly every Monday and redeemed them on the following Saturday when the week's wages had been received. Daisy herself, when times had been bad, had been one of the 'Monday morning brigade'.

Tonight, however, she had no time for such dreary thoughts. This was the last night of Jubilee Week, she had an evening off, and she was determined that she was going to enjoy every moment of it.

From One Day in Victorian England by Alastair Scott

# The pawnbroker's apprentice

Apprenticeships always lasted seven years. A youth's parents paid money to a master who then gave the youth board and lodging whilst teaching him his trade. It was very hard work for little payment. Once the seven years were up, the apprentice became a journeyman who was able to earn himself a day's wage in the trade.

In this extract, Coot is apprenticed to Mr Thompson, a pawnbroker. When people were short of money they could take along goods to be pawned for cash. These could then be redeemed (bought back) when their owner had money to do so. If at the end of a year and a day the goods had not been collected, the pawnbroker was free to sell them elsewhere.

The first customer was an ageing actor, hoping to raise five shillings on a pair of breeches that weren't worth three.

'And – and a Happy New Year to you!' he finished up, leaning over the counter with a mixture of affability and confidence through which despair showed in patches.

Coot smiled his pawnbroker's smile and began to examine the breeches with fastidious care.

'Did I leave a guinea in it, old boy?' asked the customer with pathetic jocularity as Coot turned out the pocket.

Coot said nothing; he was watching out. He pushed the breeches back to their owner.

'Ay'm afraid they ain't much use to us. A bit too far gone.'

The actor was thunderstruck. He was outraged; he was humiliated; he was bitterly dismayed. He argued, he pleaded, he begged –

'All right. A shillin', then,' interposed Coot with composure, when he judged the customer to be sufficiently low in spirits to be agreeable to anything.

'A shilling? But – '

'Try Mr Long's in 'Enrietta Street. P'raps my colleague, Mr Jeremiah Snipe, might up me a penny or two. On the other 'and, 'e might down me a sixpence. Go on. Shove off and try Mr Jeremiah.'

The pawnbroker's apprentice stared coolly at the customer, knowing him to be a beaten man. He wouldn't try Jeremiah – never in a month of Sundays! He wouldn't dare risk another such slap in the face. He was done for; he didn't even kick up much of a fuss when tuppence was knocked off his shilling: a penny for receipt and warehousing and a penny for two months' interest in advance.

'Really,' he muttered. 'That's a bit sharp, ain't it?'

For answer, Coot slid his eyes towards two framed notices that hung on the cubbyhole's wall. Decorated with the emblems of the trade, in the manner of illuminated missals, they set forth the rates of interest permitted by law and the regulations designed to protect both parties, in a lending transaction, from the sharp practice of each other.

Wearily the actor shook his head. There was no sense in wasting his eyesight on the small print. Everything was above-board, and the apprentice was as honest as an iron bar.

'I'll be back next week,' he said, taking his tenpence and mournfully patting his pawned garment, 'to redeem you, old friend.'

'Redeem? You don't know the meanin' of the word,' murmured Coot, as the customer departed into the not-quite new year.

Next came a fellow trying to pawn a wig, but the watchful apprentice found lice in it and sent him packing; and after him came a lady with the odd request that the apprentice should turn his back while she took off her petticoat hoops on which she wanted to borrow seven shillings.

'Turn me back?' said Coot, mindful of Mr Thompson's instruction to watch out. 'Ay'm afraid not. You might even nick me timepiece,' he said, laying that precious object (which his father had given him to mark the beginning of his apprenticeship) on the counter. 'I'll just sit as I am and not put temptation in your way.'

So the lady, with abject blushings, was forced to display her dirty linen and torn stockings to Coot's dreadful smile.

'Why – they ain't even real whalebone,' he said when the hoops were offered across the counter. 'Ay'm afraid they ain't much use to us. Two shillin's. That's the best.'

'You dirty little skinflint!'

'Come to think on it,' said Coot, rightly taking the expression as a personal insult, 'a shillin' and ninepence is nearer the mark.'

He pushed the hoops back. 'Or you can try Mr Long's in 'Enrietta Street. My colleague, Mr Jeremiah Snipe, might up me a penny or two. On the other 'and, 'e might down me a sixpence. Go on. Shove off and try Mr Jeremiah.'

He stared at her trembling lips and tear-filled eyes. She was done for, all right. She'd not try Jeremiah – never in a month of Sundays!

He was right, of course, he was always right; that was why Mr Thompson trusted him.

'I'll be back, of course,' said the lady, struggling to salvage some shreds of self-respect, 'to redeem them next week.'

With that, she snatched up her shilling and ninepence (less tuppence) and departed into the fast-ageing year.

Coot smiled and watched her through the window, noticing how her unsupported skirts dragged in the snow and wiped out her footprints even as she made them.

'Redeem?' he murmured. 'You don't know the meanin' of the word!'

He sat still for a moment, lost in philosophy; then he slipped from his stool, crawled under the counter, and bolted the street door. Returning, he gathered up the hoops and breeches, ticketed them, and carried them into the warehousing room at the back of the shop.

Here, in a dispiriting gloom that smelled of fallen fortunes, humbled pride, and camphor to keep off the moth, they took their places amidst a melancholy multitude of pledges awaiting redemption. Wigs, coats, gowns and sheets, walking sticks, wedding rings, shoes, and watches waited in a long and doleful queue as, month by month, they were moved up till, at the end of a year and a day, they were sold off unredeemed.

It was a grim sight, but Coot, being in the trade, was not unduly moved by it. He surveyed the crowded racks and pigeon-holes and shelves.

'Redeemed?' he whispered. 'You don't know the meanin' of the word!'

*From Apprentices by Leon Garfield*

# Treats

One thing I did like when I was a child, before I went to service, was Treats. We had three or four Treats most years, the Sunday School one in the summer and the Parish Room Christmas Treat and any others that happened to come up.

The Christmas one was carols in the Parish Room, with a word from the Vicar, and then some ladies and gentlemen playing the piano and singing or saying poetry. We liked singing the carols, but the rest was a bit beyond us. Still, it was worth it because we all had presents afterwards. We had things like knitted stockings and comforters and red calico needlecases. We always had some nuts and mince pies to take home.

One year I remember we got an orange each too. I'd never seen oranges before. I just couldn't get over all them round, golden balls heaped up by the piano with bits of holly tucked in here and there. All the kids were whispering and pointing. 'There's one each,' someone said. I don't know how I got through waiting for that concert to end. Some of the kids ate their oranges on the way home – peel and all; but we didn't (there were four of us then) we took them home for our mam along with the mince pies and the nuts.

I remember us running down the road that evening. It was frosty and misty and there were little fiery sparks when the nails on Billy's boots hit the ground. We held them golden oranges up in the air as we ran, and now and again we'd just stop in our tracks to smell them. I always take a sniff at an orange afore I peels it, even now – it's such a lovely bitterish smell.

Anyway, when we gets home mam (who knew about oranges having been in genteel service) sent me and Billy out to Mr Webb-on-the-Corner's shop for a ha'porth of *re*fined sugar. That caused some excitement straight away for we'd never seen any but the strong brown, and that not too often.

The next day being Sunday we all stood around, even dad – while mam peeled them four oranges and broke them apart. We'd never seen anything but the insides of apples and pears before, and them little purses all packed with juice made us shout aloud for pleasure. Then mam rolled the pieces in the *re*fined sugar (which is white and powdery-like) and laid them all out on her best china dish and set them in the larder to soak up the sugar.

As for the peel, that was put on a flat tin on the rack over the kitchen cooker so it could dry slowly. It dried for some days and kept the kitchen smelling lovely right over Christmas. When it was all crisp and withered mam broke it up and put it in a stone crock and used a pinch now and then to flavour a baking of hard pears or a batch of oat cakes.

But oh! The excitement of eating them sugared orange bits. We sucked them slowly and our hands got sticky. When we finished we ran our fingers round the dish and sucked the orangey sugar off them.

But, as I was saying: Treats! I recollect a Treat by the river with fireworks and baked potatoes when one of the gentry's nephews rowed in a winning boat team. Sometimes we had 'lection Treats, when someone had got into Parliament, with toffee apples for us, and beer for the grown-ups, but Sunday School Treats were the best by far.

We always had Sunday School Treats in the summer, in the garden of one of the big houses backing on the river. There'd be a big tent in case it rained, and long board tables with plates of bread-and-jam sandwiches, cut cake, buns, biscuits and slices of cheese on them, and a china wash-bowl full of radishes and lettuce leaves and half-tomatoes in the middle. It wasn't half a tuck-in!

I remember we used to sit down to tea on them sort of nasty chairs you don't see so much of nowadays – very dangerous ones that folded up sudden so you *could* nip your fingers off if you weren't lively. (Not that I remember anyone actually losing a finger, but it always added to the excitement to know it could happen.)

This Treat was for the kids who went to the Church Sunday School. The Chapels had Treats too, but nothing like so good as ours. The Chapel kids used to stand outside the big house to watch us go in and then hang about outside listening. We would make a great deal of noise, just to make them jealous, like, 'o-o-o-ooh', when they brought more cakes in, and 'hooray' when we'd finished eating.

All the food was sent in by the people from the genteel families who went to our church. Good, nice plain stuff and plenty of it. They sent their servants to help too and it made us feel very rich having our mugs filled up by maids in white aprons.

Some of the big boys would call, 'More, more!' when a plate was empty, but our family never did. We knew it was very rude.

After tea we ran races, and gentlemen took us for a row up the river, or got the boys doing tug-o'-war. Before we went home we took a dip in a bran tub for little presents wrapped in pink paper. I remember I once got a little 'broidered thing full of hairpins, and our Charlie had a lady's cardcase with the lock broke off. I suppose they'd been sent in by ladies who didn't want them any longer – like for rummage sales nowadays. Still, we were grateful, it was so nice getting anything!

From A Strong and Willing Girl by Dorothy Edwards

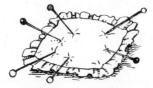

# Meals and manners

This extract is from Lark Rise to Candleford. The author, Flora Thompson, writes about growing up in a small hamlet on the Oxfordshire-Northamptonshire border during the last years of Queen Victoria's reign. In this piece we learn about meals and manners in 'poor people's houses'.

Here, then, were the three chief ingredients of the one hot meal a day, bacon from the flitch, vegetables from the garden, and flour for the roly-poly. This meal, called 'tea' was taken in the evening, when the men were home from the fields and the children from school, for neither could get home at midday.

About four o'clock, smoke would go up from the chimneys, as the fire was made up and the big iron boiler, or the three-legged pot, was slung on the hook of the chimney-chain. Everything was cooked in the one utensil; the square of bacon, amounting to little more than a taste each; cabbage, or other green vegetables in one net, potatoes in another, and the roly-poly swathed in a cloth. It sounds a haphazard method in these days of gas and electric cookers; but it answered its purpose, for, by carefully timing the putting in of each item and keeping the simmering of the pot well regulated, each item was kept intact and an appetising meal was produced. The water in which the food had been cooked, the potato parings, and other vegetable trimmings were the pig's share.

When the men came home from work they would find the table spread with a clean whitey-brown cloth, upon which would be knives and two-pronged steel forks with buckhorn handles. The vegetables would then be turned out into big round yellow crockery dishes and the bacon cut into dice, with much the largest cube upon Feyther's plate, and the whole family would sit down to the chief meal of the day. True, it was seldom that all could find places at the central table; but some of the smaller children could sit upon stools with the seat of a chair for a table, or on the doorstep with their plates on their laps.

Good manners prevailed. The children were given their share of the food, there was no picking and choosing, and they were expected to eat it in silence. 'Please' and 'Thank you' were permitted, but nothing more. Father and Mother might talk if they wanted to; but usually they were content to concentrate upon their enjoyment of the meal. Father might shovel green peas into his mouth with his knife, Mother might drink her tea from her saucer, and some of the children might lick their plates when the food was devoured; but who could eat peas with a two-pronged fork, or wait for tea to cool after the heat and flurry of cooking, and licking the plates passed as a graceful compliment to Mother's good dinner. 'Thank God for my good dinner. Thank Father and Mother. Amen' was the grace used in one family, and it certainly had the merit of giving credit where credit was due.

For other meals they depended largely on bread and butter, or, more often, bread and lard, eaten with any relish that happened to be at hand. Fresh butter was too costly for general use, but a pound was sometimes purchased in the summer, when it cost tenpence. Margarine, then called 'butterine', was already on the market, but was little used there, as most people preferred lard, especially when it was their own home-made lard flavoured with rosemary leaves. In summer there was always plenty of green food from the garden and home-made jam as long as it lasted, and sometimes an egg or two, where fowls were kept, or when eggs were plentiful and sold at twenty a shilling.

When bread and lard appeared alone, the men would spread mustard on their slices and the children would be given a scraping of black treacle or a sprinkling of brown sugar. Some children, who preferred it, would have 'sop' – bread steeped in boiling water, then strained and sugar added.

Milk was a rare luxury, as it had to be fetched a mile and a half from the farmhouse. The cost was not great: a penny a jug or can, irrespective of size. It was, of course, skimmed milk, but hand-skimmed, not separated, and so still had some small proportion of cream left. A few families fetched it daily, but many did not bother about it. The women said they preferred their tea neat, and it did not seem to occur to them that the children needed milk. Many of them never tasted it from the time they were weaned until they went out in the world. Yet they were stout-limbed and rosy-cheeked and full of life and mischief.

The skimmed milk was supposed by the farmer to be sold at a penny a pint, that remaining unsold going to feed his own calves and pigs. But the dairymaid did not trouble to measure it; she just filled the proffered vessel and let it go as a 'pen'orth.'

From Lark Rise to Candleford by Flora Thompson

# In 1884

### Lizzie Robbins, aged 9
### Flower-seller

Lives in a basement room with her mother and three younger brothers. Her mother earns 10 shillings (50p) weekly as a factory cleaner. One brother, aged 7, earns 3d a week (just over 1p) running errands. Her father has left home, but occasionally sends the family a little money.

Lizzie attends a Mission school most days. In the evening she buys cheap (faded) violets from a flower-seller in Piccadilly, and then walks round the theatre and restaurant districts, selling bunches at 2½d (1p) each. She returns home about midnight, and gives the money to her mother. A night's earnings average about 8p.

### Millie Pearson, aged 10
### Match-seller

Lives in two rooms in Lambeth, with her parents and four younger brothers and sisters. Two other children died in infancy. Her father, a skilled carpenter, earns 29 shillings a week (£1.45). Millie attends a charity school, and sells matches outside the pubs near her home on summer evenings and Saturdays. The matches are long-headed 'fusees' and sell at one penny (less than ½p) for a box of twenty.

In the winter Millie helps her mother at night with sewing and mending for private customers.

### Henry John McNaughton, aged 11
### Paper-delivery boy

The eldest of three children, Henry lives with them and his mother in one room. Father's whereabouts unknown. Henry's mother earns 10 shillings a week

(50p) as a charwoman in a private house, and can occasionally bring home left-over food.

Henry attends a Board School, which costs 9d weekly (about 3p). He does one paper round before school and another at night, and earns 3d (just over 1p) a day. This pays for his schooling, and his mother has the rest for the upkeep of the family.

### William Jones, aged 10
### Crossing-sweeper

(A hundred years ago the roads were cobbled or dirt-surfaced, pot-holed and puddled. All vehicles were drawn by horses or donkeys, so the roads were very dirty, and crossing-sweepers were an important part of town life.)

William shares a pitch across a busy shopping street with his brother George, aged 11. Every pedestrian who uses their crossing gives a halfpenny tip. In bad weather the boys can earn 10 shillings (50p) a day, in good weather much less.

William and George should attend school, but never have. Neither can read or write. Their father is dead and their mother abandoned them. At night they sleep in a ramshackle empty house, with a tribe of other homeless boys.

Faith Jaques

# Illness in the family

Annie Beatrice Champion was born in 1855, the seventh of ten children. She discovered a natural talent for looking after children when her mother died young and she was put in charge of her younger brothers and sisters at the age of twelve. She then embarked on a long career as a nanny for wealthy families and was given the nickname 'Pettie' by some of the children she looked after.
In this extract from her reminiscences, Pettie tells of her own childhood when she was seriously ill with typhoid.

One day my eldest brother came home from school feeling ill – it was scarlet fever. We all caught it excepting my father, mother and elder sister. Mine turned to typhoid; I was very ill, went into a trance and was supposed to have died (I was measured for my coffin on the second day evening). My mother was restless as she was expecting a baby and her maternity nurse, who had nursed her through all her children's births, gave up all her engagements and came to help my mother with us. My mother wanted to come in the next room to see me, she kept saying 'I am sure she is not dead; I am sure the Almighty would not take her after all my care and prayers.' Nurse thought she was going out of her mind with grief and sent for Doctor Saunders. He was out so Doctor Firman, his partner, came. Nurse was obliged to bring my mother in to see me. I had been put in the front parlour to save my mother coming up and down stairs. She said 'Take that handkerchief off her face', the nurse was trying to get her to take a glass of wine, she took it from her and poured it into my mouth and down my throat. Nurse was astonished to see my throat move and, after a little while, my eyelids flicker. Doctor Firman came in just then and stayed with me all night. I can remember lying still when ill, hearing sobbing and talking, but I could not move. I think this must have been when I was in my trance. Then came a very long time of getting well, as doctors Firman and Saunders said that I was not yet 'out of the bush'. My family called me 'the little dead girl' until I was grown up in my teens, and our doctor always called me that.

Before I was well my little brother had arrived. Feeling ill with scarlet fever I wanted my mother. Doctor Saunders said 'Your mother is not well. I have brought her a baby to make her better!' 'Bring me a baby and it will make me better' I said, 'So I will' he said, 'that is a splendid idea. You make haste and get better, and I will take you to see my Baby Tree. But now you must eat lots of custard and milk puddings and drink up your soup.' I can remember that I used to ask for pudding every day, but was too ill to eat it. I felt sick and could not eat, but I always said 'Don't tell Doctor Saunders that I did not eat my pudding.' I was terrified that I should not get the baby he had promised me. I can remember asking him every day when he came if he had got one in his pocket. When I asked him where he found them he said 'Under my Baby Tree', and explained how he dug them up with a golden spade and put them in his pocket. At last the novelty wore off. I fretted, and was carried upstairs, bed and all, by my father, Doctor Firman and Doctor Saunders, and placed beside my mother's bed. I was next to my baby brother's cot with its old fashioned walnut wood frame, deep sacking bottom, white dimity lining and curtains. This baby satisfied me and I forgot to ask any more for my own one.

From Pettie – Memories of a Victorian Nursery by Annie Beatrice Champion

# Me and my family

I was born in Wilberfoss, a little village a few miles east of York, in 1906 and christened Nancy Elizabeth Gillah. I was the seventh of nine children – all girls.

We were a happy family. We had plenty to eat and we enjoyed one another's company. Our life was our home and the village. We didn't think much about the outside world. In those days, there was no television, no radio, no telephone and no cars or buses.

We lived at Hope House, Middle Street. It was double-fronted, with an enormous garden at the back. The front room on the right was our playroom. The front room on the left was the living room. Down a passage was a big kitchen with a range, and two dairies. In one dairy, we kept the crockery and all the pies and puddings. In the other dairy, which was cooler, we kept big bowls of milk and eggs as well as a churn for making butter.

Upstairs were five bedrooms. My parents had the biggest one. I shared a room with my two younger sisters, Joyce and Mary. I had a single bed and they shared a double bed. My two elder sisters shared another bedroom and two live-in maids shared the bedroom next door. There was a spare bedroom for when one of us was ill.

Each bedroom had a washstand and a chamber pot. We had no running water in the house and the lavatory was outside. There were oil lamps in the downstairs rooms, but we went to bed by candlelight.

There were several outbuildings next to the house. There was a stable for our horse, Mabel, and two coach-houses for the trap and the gig. There was a wash-house with a big copper, a coal store, a pigsty and some cowsheds.

There was a pump outside where we fetched water for drinking and cooking. In the winter, it was covered with sacking to stop the water from freezing. There were also three corrugated iron tanks at the corners of the house, to collect soft rainwater off the roof for washing. The water was heated in huge pans over a coal fire or in the wash-house copper.

On Sundays, we went to church both morning and evening. Father was one of the church wardens. We sat with our grandfather in the front pew directly below the pulpit.

Grandfather was a rich farmer, who rather thought of himself as the local squire. When he went out, he always dressed very smartly in a frock coat and a silk hat and had a big pocket-watch. If he felt the sermon was going on too long, he would fetch out his watch as a signal to the vicar to stop.

On Sunday afternoons, we went to Sunday School. There was no Sunday School for our church so we went to the Methodist Sunday School instead. Every week, I learned a poem off by heart.

Afterwards, I went to visit my grandmother who lived at Newton Lodge, about a mile-and-a-half from Wilberfoss. I walked there on my own. Usually, I took her a piece of cake for her tea and some pale pink wool for her knitting. She used to knit all our vests.

She always wore a black velvet dress and a little white lace hat. She suffered very badly from arthritis, so she lived in one room on the ground floor and had a housekeeper to look after her and the house.

From 'When I Was Young' (Early 20th Century) Ruth Thomson meets Nancy Emery

# BRITAIN SINCE 1930

# A kitchen in the early 1930s

The house where I grew up had no central heating, and no hot water in the tap. In the early 1930s, the warmest room in a house was usually the kitchen. After getting out of bed, and putting cold feet on the linoleum covered floor, it was good to come into the kitchen and to a glowing fire.

The fire was kept in during wintertime, in the big, black, kitchen range which was made of cast iron. This range was brushed and polished with blacklead every day, until it shone. The fire heated an oven in the range, and a lid about eight inches in diameter was lifted off the top. This let out the heat from the fire, and was where a kettle of water for general use was kept constantly boiling.

A large, wooden table where food was prepared and eaten stood in one corner. This gleamed almost white from the constant scrubbing by mother, who used a bristle brush, and a block of carbolic soap for disinfectant. This table also served as a desk when I did my schoolwork. The chairs too, were wooden, although father's was special, with curved armrests and a high back.

A black fender with a brass rail stood in front of the range. This rail, and the brass tongs used for lifting knobs of coal from the coal scuttle were polished daily. An iron poker laid in the hearth, was used to riddle the ashes as the coal burned away.

In the scullery (a small room leading off the kitchen), a stone copper was filled with cold water on washing days and bath nights. A small fire was lit in the grate beneath it, and the water slowly heated up.

In summertime, a smaller fire was kept in the kitchen range, sufficient to keep pans or a kettle boiling on top. It was during winter evenings that the fire was most appreciated, when the family sat and listened to the wireless. Outside the ice froze on the windowpanes, but in the kitchen it was warm and cheerful by the range where the coal fire glowed.

Doris Corti

# Bath night

There was always a palaver in our kitchen on a Friday night. At exactly eight o'clock the curtains were drawn and every possible container – kettles, bowls, pans – was filled to the brim with cold water. I had to watch they didn't boil over on the cooker while Mum went downstairs and out into the back-yard to struggle all the way up with the big tin bath.

I always felt sorry for that tin bath. All the week it hung outside on the shed door, neglected in all weathers. On a rainy night we were kept awake with the monotonous tune of drops tap-dancing and drumming on it, but still it hung there, rain-rusted and speckled white with bird droppings. However, once a week it was brought into the warm kitchen and there, for a few hours, it was fussed over like a new-born babe. It was welcomed upstairs only, though, for downstairs I heard the sound of bass booming as it banged against furniture and corners.

I stood on a chair and undressed while Mum cleaned out the bath, but it was so big and took such a long time that it was never done properly. I got used to sitting on the gritty bottom and always expected to see a couple of drowned spiders floating on the surface.

By this time there was so much steam in the kitchen I could hardly see Mum lift off the containers to pour them in the bath.

'Mind out or you'll get splashed!' she screamed, her voice almost drowned by the great gushing hot waterfall.

When the bath was filled enough so that the water would at least cover my legs, Ibcol and soda were thrown in, and then it was ready to receive me.

One toe in: 'OUCH! Ooh, it's too hot, Mum. Put in some cold.' Only a basinful was thrown in because Mum had to come in after me while it was still hot, so that she could sweat out a week's stink of onion. The

worst part about having a bath was sitting down; I tentatively plunged down but was up much quicker; my goodness it was hot, it made my heart beat all over my body. I held onto the handle at the end of the bath and bent up and down, sitting down a little further each time.

'Will you stop messing about? We haven't got all night, and you're making that water cold.'

When I wasn't looking Mum pushed my bottom down and before I could scream, I found I was in. There was no time to enjoy the luxury of warm water, for to Mum bathing was a business, not a pleasure. She washed my back while I was supposed to wash my front, but I liked to blow bubbles.

'You can stop that lark, Valerie. I've told you to hurry up. As if we haven't got enough soap and water over the floor already. Be all right if it's dripping onto the Old Man's head downstairs, wouldn't it? Now have you washed yourself properly?'

'Yes, Mum. Let me blow one more bubble.'

'There's no time for mucking about. You can blow as many bubbles as you like when we have a proper bath. Right, then, that's you finished, thank the Lord. Now come on out, I've got the towel ready.'

From London Morning by Valerie Avery

# Starting work

When I left school at fourteen I got a job through my uncle. He was the delivery man for the local bakery. I worked on the bread deliveries from seven in the morning until six in the evening, Monday to Thursday. Then on Friday and Saturday I worked until nine-thirty in the evening. For all this I earned seven shillings and sixpence a week. After a few months I started in the bake-house wheeling sacks of flour for fifteen shillings a week.

When I was fifteen my father had an accident in the colliery and broke both his legs. He was off work for some time and we didn't have enough to live on.

My wage from the bakery wasn't much so I went along, cap in hand, to the colliery manager to ask for a job. He said, 'Does your father work here?' I said, 'Yes, sir.' He asked me my father's name and when I told him he said, 'Start on Monday.'

Father didn't want me to work down the pit so he was furious. If he'd been able to get out of bed he'd have stopped me going to see the manager.

I earned £1 2s. 6d. for a six day week. There were no guaranteed wages. If the pit was closed for any reason we got no money. We worked shifts of seven-and-a-half hours. You couldn't work the night shift until you were fifteen.

We had a twenty minute break for food which we took underground with us. I had bread and jam, or cheese sometimes. The jam kept the bread nice and moist.

From When I Was Young: The Thirties by Neil Thompson and Glynn Davies

# The wireless set

One of our proud possessions in the nineteen twenties and thirties was our wireless set. It was what we now call a radio. It was called a wireless set at that time because before its invention all messages and sounds had been sent along wires. But the wireless could send and receive messages through the air. Something we found quite remarkable. It still is if you think about it. One of the reasons for our pride was that not many people had wireless sets at the time as you could not buy them in the shops. But you could buy one of those 'Do-it-yourself' magazines that told you how to make one. My father did just that.

What could we hear on the wireless set? I remember that at about six o'clock in the evening as the daylight faded and we waited for my father to come home from work, we listened to dance band music played by Jack Paine's or Henry Hall's bands. There were songs such as 'The Man on the Flying Trapeze' and 'Wheezy Anna', and 'Here's to the Next Time' at the end of the Henry Hall programme. On Saturdays there would be variety concerts with singers, comedians and other entertainers. Arthur Askey, Clapham and Dwyer, Elsie and Doris Walters and Claude Dampier were some of their names. If you ever come across old copies of the comic *Radio Fun* you could get some idea of what they were like. There was also a programme called *In Town Tonight* in which they would pretend to bring London's traffic to a halt in order to talk to people. This was so well done that for a long time I thought it actually happened!

But my favourite programme as a child was *Children's Hour*. This would be at tea time and there were thrilling dramatisations of stories like *Treasure Island* and *Moonfleet.* Though when I was young I liked *Toytown* best with its stories of Larry the Lamb, Earnest the Policeman, Mr Grouser, Mr Mayor and Dennis the Dachshund. Uncle Mac and Uncle David used to present *Children's Hour* and Uncle David would take the part of Larry the Lamb with his sad little bleating voice. They would also wish you a happy birthday if your parents wrote in to let them know when it was. You can tell from that that there could not have been all that number of wireless sets around. If it was a twins' birthday they used to add 'Hallo Twins!'

One snag with the wireless set was that from time to time it suffered from what my father called 'oscillation'. Then it would make terrible screechy wailing noises as if it was in pain! And when this happened you did not hear anything else!

It was the War in 1939 that saw the end of our wireless set and the introduction of a radio into the house. My father worked for the Air Ministry and was told there could be important messages sent out over the radio to those who worked for the Government. So he thought, just in case, he had better have a more reliable set not subject to 'oscillation'. So one of those domed bakelite radios took the place of our wireless set in our back room.

John Cotton

# August 1939

'Dear Mr Hitler,' wrote the child,
'Please don't have a war.' Struggling
with spelling she wasn't sure
if WAR looked right, but

since Hitler spoke in German
perhaps it wouldn't matter.
Her letter must be brief, polite,
to make him think again.

They were driving home from holiday
through the dusty yellow days
of August. Grown-up conversation
had been boringly of war. She

didn't know quite what they meant.
It made them melancholy,
abrupt in their unease,
and she was frightened too.

Gas masks had been issued. Inside
they smelled of kitchen soap
and rubber. In stuffy privacy
she practised for the promised war

by writing Hitler's letter
through the plastic window,
'Please don't drop your bombs on us.
We don't want to die.'

She couldn't think of how to finish.
It wouldn't do to send her love,
so she just wrote her name,
'From Moira Brown' – and posted it.

Moira Andrew

# War rhymes

These rhymes were used for skipping or chanting by children.

When the war is over
Hitler will be dead
He hopes to go to Heaven
With his halo on his head
But the Lord says NO
YOU'LL HAVE TO GO BELOW
THERE'S ONLY ROOM FOR CHURCHILL
SO CHEERY CHEERY OH!

Underneath the churchyard, six feet deep,
There lies Hitler fast asleep,
All the little mice come and tickle his feet,
'Neath the churchyard, six feet deep.

Who's that knocking at the window?
Who's that knocking at the door?
If it's Hitler, let him in
And we'll sit him on a pin,
And we won't see old Hitler any more.

Anonymous

## How Evacuation is Working

# 40,000 DOING LESSONS IN THEIR HOMES

### BY OUR OWN CORRESPONDENT

SHEFFIELD, Tuesday.

*UNTIL the Sheffield schools reopen, children are being taught in groups in houses, and teachers go on their rounds from house to house.*

By next Monday it is likely that 40,000 children will be doing their school work at home.

Mothers have moved furniture and even beds to make room for classes.

I found ten boys with their heads bowed over the table in the front room of one house, and a teacher taking charge.

One boy said he was glad to start his lessons again.

'We like holidays but this has been too long,' he said. 'It's nice to have something to do again.'

Mr T. E. Hepworth, headmaster at a new housing estate with 1,230 schoolchildren, said he had been delighted with the response from mothers.

'We cannot expect any great academic successes through this home system,' he commented, 'but it is proving an invaluable link between teachers, parents and scholars which may be useful when peace comes.

'The school is used as a base and teachers each morning draw what equipment they may need for the day's lessons.

'Each teacher goes from one group to another.

'Naturally we cannot give science and other technical lessons, as at school, but our main point is that we keep the children's minds active.

'The curriculum includes speech training, the recital of little plays and other items of an entertaining nature.

'On fine days arithmetic will be taught on rambles by the children striding certain distances and measuring them up, and by other methods.'

# LONELY, LEFT IN LONDON

### By RITCHIE CALDER

**ARCHIE APPLEBY was feeling sorry for himself. He hung disconsolately over the parapet of London Bridge, gazing down on the traffic in the Pool, when I spoke to him.**

Archie is not quite 13, and he is one of the thousands of schoolchildren left behind in London when the others were evacuated.

'Why didn't you go with the rest?' I asked him.

'I wanted to,' he said, with a choke in his voice. 'But when they broadcast about the evacuation Dad and Mum and me were on holiday. They said "not to rush back, but stay where we were." And we did.

'Now all the billets from my school are filled and I can't get away until the next lot goes. Maybe I won't get with my chums after all...'

Archie is one of the 8,000 London County Council children registered for the second evacuation, but awaiting Government orders.

# Evacuees

Neville, Danny, Zuckerman and Winkler are members of a class of boys that have been evacuated from Manchester to Blackpool with their teacher Mr Goldstone, who is trying to find accommodation for them.

Scene 17. Exterior, Blackpool, street 'A'. Afternoon.
(*Coming up the street – away from the promenade (indicated, perhaps, by a promenade 'pagoda' shelter) is most of* **Danny's** *class, led by* **Mr Goldstone,** *and including* **Neville.**
*They walk up the residential street, in a crocodile, each boy carrying a tin of corned beef, as well as his case (or haversack) and gas-mask case. Some of them are fitfully singing 'Ten Green Bottles' or 'Michael Finnegan'.* **Zuckerman** *is wearing his gas-mask.*)

Scene 18. Exterior, Blackpool, street 'B'.
(*The crocodile of boys walk along,* **Zuckerman** *still wearing his gas-mask. An air-raid siren begins to wail. The boys look up at the sky, apprehensively. The singing stops*).

| | |
|---|---|
| **Mr Goldstone:** | It's not an air-raid. They're just trying the sirens out. They do it every afternoon. It's a practice. |
| **Neville:** *(to Danny)* | We've heard *that* one before. |
| **Danny:** | Yes, he can tell that to the marines, can't he? (*Hoping for appreciation.*) I said he can tell that to the marines, didn't I? |

(*The crocodile comes to a halt, while* **Mr Goldstone** *enters a garden gate and starts up the path to a house.*
At the window of the neighbouring house, a woman's face appears at the parted curtain, looks horrified at the boys, and disappears again, as the curtains are closed.
**Mr Goldstone** *rings the doorbell of her neighbour.*)

| | |
|---|---|
| **Mr Goldstone:** *(without looking round)* | Take it off, Zuckerman. *(**Zuckerman** takes off his gas-mask. The door opens and a young **Housewife** appears. She takes in the scene, suspiciously.)* Good afternoon, madam. My name is Mr Goldstone. I'm a teacher from … |
| **First housewife:** *(hastily)* | I can't take no evacuees! |
| **Mr Goldstone:** | Oh. |
| **First housewife:** *(guiltily)* | I'd like to. Only … um … *(she tries to think of an excuse.)* Only I have this invalid father. Sorry. *(**Mr Goldstone** smiles his acknowledgement. She closes the door, and he returns to his charges. They start to tramp off to the next house.)* |
| **Danny:** | I hate Her Hitler. *('Her' mispronounced as written.)* |
| **Neville:** *(correcting him)* | 'Herr' Hitler. |
| **Danny:** | What? |
| **Neville:** | It's 'Herr' not 'Her'. |
| **Danny:** *(defeated)* | Sometimes, it's Her. |
| **Neville:** | Never. |
| **Danny:** | It can be. It's irrelevant. *(Cut to **Mr Goldstone** at the next door, talking to **Second housewife**)* |
| **Second housewife:** | Sorry, I only wish I could. *(Thinks for a moment.)* Only I have three of my own, you see. Well, four, really. |
| **Mr Goldstone:** | Three or four? |
| **Second housewife:** | Four. All told. It wouldn't be doing right by them. |
| **Mr Goldstone:** | Thank you madam. Good day. |
| **Second housewife:** | Not at all. Pleasure to be of help. *(She closes the door.)* |

Scene 19. Exterior, Blackpool, street 'C'.
*(A couple of hours later.*
*The crocodile is now somewhat shorter – and much more weary. The boys trudge along either dragging their cases or bent double by their haversacks – still clutching their tins of corned beef.*
*Cut to* **Mr Goldstone** *talking to* **Third housewife** *on her doorstep.)*

| | |
|---|---|
| **Third housewife:**<br>*(surveying the boys doubtfully)* | Are they clean? |
| **Mr Goldstone:**<br>*(wearily)* | Oh, yes, madam. We have to evacuate the cleanest first, by Act of Parliament. |
| **Third housewife:** | What? |
| **Mr Goldstone:** | They're all very clean. |
| **Third housewife:** | Go on, then. I'll try one. |
| **Mr Goldstone:** | Thank you, madam. Which?<br>*(She stands, surveying the boys – like a cattle market.*<br>*The boys stand looking back at her – some thrusting their chests and faces forward hoping to be chosen, others too tired and past caring.*<br>**Zuckerman** *pulls his tongue at her.)* |
| **Third housewife:** | That one. *(She points to* **Neville**.*)* |
| **Mr Goldstone:** | Sorry. He's one of a pair. |
| **Third housewife:** | Eh? |
| **Mr Goldstone:** | He's with his brother. We try not to separate brothers. |
| **Third housewife:** | I can't take *two...* |
| **Mr Goldstone:** | Can I interest you in one of the others perhaps? |
| **Third housewife:** | He'll do.<br>*(She points at* **Winkler**.<br>**Mr Goldstone** *pushes* **Winkler** *to her and gives them both thick sheaves of paper bearing typed instructions and advice.)* |
| **Mr Goldstone:** | Say hello to the lady. |
| **Winkler:** | Hello. |
| **Mr Goldstone:**<br>*(while writing down the woman's address on his clipboard)* | This is Cyril Winkler. |
| **Third housewife:**<br>*(to Winkler)* | That's a funny name isn't it? |
| **Mr Goldstone:** | Say yes. |
| **Winkler:** | Yes. |
| **Third housewife:**<br>*(pulling* Winkler's *shirt collar down slightly)* | Got a tide-mark as well, haven't you? *(She ushers him in and closes the door).* |

From Evacuees by Jack Rosenthal

# Like foreigners to us

One evening, in the autumn of 1940, an evacuated woman from London and her two sons walked through our front gate, introduced themselves and moved in. The sons were about the same ages as my brother and myself and at first we were excited to have them living in our house. But I'm afraid we didn't get on very well with each other. Although London was only about 250 miles away, the evacuees were almost like foreigners to us. I expect we seemed the same to them. In those days most people could not afford to travel very far from home, and none of my family had been to London. The evacuees had never been anywhere else. As a result, we did not know much about each other's way of life. For instance, I had never heard of baked beans until one day the woman opened a tin she had bought and gave me some to try. I thought they were the most delicious food I had ever tasted. They lived off tinned food much of the time, but we had hardly seen it. On the other hand, they were surprised to see chickens wandering about in the garden and cows grazing in the fields around us.

So both families were a bit suspicious of each other. The evacuees thought New Hedges a very dull place and probably regarded us as primitive peasants. In fact, they certainly did hold some very uncomplimentary opinions about Wales and the Welsh. For our part, we considered the evacuees rude and rough. We thought it very strange that the younger boy used to go to bed with his boots on and that they all slept downstairs in the same room, even though there was a bedroom upstairs which the boys could have used.

The evacuees stayed with us for about eight months and then decided to go home. I think they found life in New Hedges so boring that they preferred to be back in London, despite the danger. But it showed us how lucky we were that we were not forced by bombing to leave our home and go to live in an unfamiliar place. Other evacuees, however, enjoyed being in a different part of the country, and some liked it so much that they never went home, even after the war was over.

From Children at War edited by Patricia Williams

# from 'Autobiography'

Carrying my gas-mask to school every day
buying saving stamps
remembering my National Registration Number
(ZMGM/136/3 see I can still remember it)
avoiding Careless Talk Digging for Victory
looking for German spies everywhere
Oh yes, I did my bit for my country that long dark winter,
me and Winston and one or two others,
wearing my tin hat whenever possible
Singing 'Hang out the Washing on the Siegfried Line'
aircraft-recognition charts pinned to my bedroom wall
the smell of paint on toy soldiers
doing paintings of Spitfires and Hurricanes, Lancasters and Halifaxes
along with a Heinkel or a Messerschmitt plunging helplessly into the
sea in the background

pink light in the sky from Liverpool burning fifty miles away
the thunder of daylight flying fortresses high overhead shaking the
elderberry tree
bright barrage-balloons flying over the docks
morning curve of the bay seen from the park on the hill
after coming out of the air-raid shelter
listening for the 'All Clear' siren
listening to Vera Lynn Dorothy Lamour Allan Jones and the Andrews
Sisters
clutching my father's hand tripping over the unfamiliar kerb
I walk over every day
in the black-out

Adrian Henri

# Lessons in the air-raid shelter

Our village had never been bombed but the Headmaster said that we had to be prepared. So every Wednesday afternoon he walked along the school corridors ringing the hand bell over and over again and we had to pretend there was an air-raid. It was like fire drill is today but much more fun!

As the bell clanged up and down the corridors we all grabbed our gas-masks and filed neatly out in twos, across the playground and into the underground shelter.

It wasn't really under the ground; it was an Anderson shelter, built of curved metal and covered with grassy banks. But as you went into the blackness it felt like going under the earth. It smelt like it too, dank and damp. Half-blinded, we stumbled along wooden duck-boards down to the end of the long, arched shelter. Ahead of us, the teacher lit paraffin lamps, hung along the roof bars and we looked for a place on the benches which ran along the sides of the shelter, right side for boys, left for girls. There was lots of chattering and giggling and swapping of places but as soon as the Headmaster shut the door with a great clang, we were silent and still. We sat waiting for our orders.

'Gas masks...OUT!' The Headmaster yelled at us like a sergeant-major at his troops.

We scrabbled in our little cardboard boxes, pulled out the gas mask and held the rubber straps at the ready for the next order:

'Gas masks...ON!'

This was the difficult bit. The rubber straps got tangled in your hair and pulled it painfully. The metal snout often hit your nose. The celluloid visor always misted up so you could see even less in the flickering lamp-light. And worst of all, once you snapped the mask down under your chin, there was an awful moment when you felt as if you'd never be able to breathe again.

And we were supposed to get into the mask in one minute flat! We always tried very hard because if we were in time we could have a barley sugar. Free sweets were a great treat in those days of rationing.

After we'd taken off our gas-masks – in ten seconds flat! – and sucked our sweets, it was time for the singing lesson. That was the only lesson we ever had in the air-raid shelter. I suppose it was the easiest thing to do with the two hundred children crammed side-by-side in the semi-darkness.

So that's what we did every Wednesday afternoon, after playtime, for years. I was in the juniors by the time a real air-raid happened. And that was on a Friday, after dinner.

We all went home for dinner then, but most of us rushed back for a game of hopscotch, skipping or endless games of 'tiggy'. You couldn't play with a gas-mask bumping on your chest, so we used to pile them up on the steps at the school entrance.

So that Friday afternoon, when the sirens wailed out, the playground was full of rushing, grabbing, laughing children, like some great party. We didn't even hear the air-raid warning, after all the real air-raids happened at night. It was only when the Headmaster came running amongst us clanging his bell that we fell silent. And heard the stomach-churning noise of the siren.

Urged on by the Headmaster, we raced to the door of the air-raid shelter and tried to push our way in. Only one teacher had arrived back and she had opened the door, ready to count us in. Some hope! We squeezed through, three and four at a time, some getting stuck, others pushed out, howling in panic. And all the time the sirens wailed and the Headmaster's bell clanged.

Inside was even worse. None of the lanterns was lit, so we scrambled for seats, in the darkness, squirming and wriggling our bottoms into any space we could find, left-side or right-side, shrieking and giggling as we fell on someone's knee. It was all so exciting that we never thought to be afraid.

There was no point in doing a count; many children would have stayed at home anyway. So as soon as the door was shut, and a few of the lanterns lit, the Headmaster went straight into the gas mask drill.

But most of our gas masks were outside on the steps! Luckily it was quite dark, so the few who had gas masks with them made a great to-do of flapping them out and putting them on, and those of us without just did all the actions. It was so dark, and I suppose the Headmaster was so worried about the raid, that he didn't seem to notice.

Gas masks were on and off in record time and we all sat back to wait for the barley sugars. But there was only a pause. The Headmaster just stood looking along the lines of children, faces turned towards him, waiting for their reward.

It never came. Like our gas masks, the sweet tin had been left behind in the rush! We passed the terrible news down the lines, like a game of Chinese whispers, and some of the infants' children started to cry.

Then our teacher quickly struck up with 'Run, rabbit, run, rabbit, run, run run!' and we rather raggedly joined in. After that there was no stopping us; we sang and sang until we had hardly any voices left and the 'All Clear' went. We trooped out into the playground, blinking in the sunlight, stumbling up the school steps, fumbling for our gas masks.

Later we heard there had been no raid that afternoon; it was a false alarm. We didn't mind about that; it had been more exciting than mental arithmetic. But what about the barley-sugars? Somebody said we'd get them at playtime. But, do you know what? We didn't even get a playtime!

Bette Paul

# Interview: Mrs Ivy Green, Ramsgate

During the Blitz in World War II, the safest places for people to escape the bombing were deep underground shelters where no bombs could penetrate. Londoners sheltered from the bombs in the tube stations, sleeping on the platforms. People in Nottingham made use of a system of natural caves beneath the town.

Ramsgate in Kent is one of only two towns in Europe to have purpose built deep shelters. (The other is Barcelona which withstood some of the heaviest bombing of the Spanish Civil War). Work started on Ramsgate's tunnels in the spring of 1939. A central tunnel, which had previously brought the railway to Ramsgate seafront, was expanded and linked to many smaller passages. The chalk on which Ramsgate is built was very easy to cut and needed no propping. Work was completed just before war broke out and the system stretched for three miles at an average depth of 67 feet. There were 22 entrances and the whole population of Ramsgate could shelter in safety.

I interviewed Mrs Ivy Green, who was eleven years old when war began and spent much of the first three years of the war living in these tunnels.

### When did you first go down the tunnels?
The first time I went down the tunnels was on the 24th August 1940 after a very heavy air raid when the gas works blew up. There were only about six children in Ramsgate at the time, all the rest having been evacuated, but my father worked at the gas works and he wasn't allowed to move. So we all stayed. My mum said that if a bomb got one of us it would get the family.

### Can you describe the tunnels?
There was a large central tunnel and a system of smaller ones that led into it from entrances around the town. The main tunnel was actually used by a miniature railway before the war began, and those of us who were sheltering there would sleep in deck chairs or blankets on either side of the tracks. As time went on, huts were constructed from black sacking, we were number 71. The huts were different sizes, larger ones with double bunks for families and smaller areas for couples. The bunks were really comfortable. My sister was in the top one, my younger sister and I in the bottom one and Mum and Dad in a bed that they'd taken down there.

### So you began to think of the tunnels as home?
My mother put curtains round the chalky walls and across the door to make it private and homely. We had lino on the floor. We had the cat and the budgie down there, and a radio. The mums were always sweeping and polishing. We cooked on primus stoves – the collection of different cooking smells was amazing, as were the meals that mothers prepared. My dad used to come to the tunnels straight from work and that was home.

### Could you hear anything of what was going on at the surface?

If there was a raid up top we'd hear a plonk and the place would shake. If the bomb was a big 1000 pounder and it landed above where we were, the lights would go out and soot used to blow down from the roof.

### What were the tunnel entrances like?

Entrances to the tunnels were mostly wide and well-lit. We went down about ten or twelve flights of steps to the passages. The seafront end of the main tunnel was open to begin with but it was eventually blocked up to prevent the Germans from gaining access if they ever invaded.

### As a child, how did you adapt to life underground?

We made our own amusements. We'd go up the passages and carve our names in the chalk. We did sewing and took comics down. For an 'afternoon out' we'd walk though the tunnels to a canteen that was established near Dumpton station. There were no schools in operation at that time so my father taught us what little he could.

### Can you recall any special events?

My sister had a party in the tunnels for her eighth birthday. We rummaged together and everyone gave a little bit of their ration. At Christmas too there were parties for the children – everything 'make do and mend'. Jellies were made from gelatine and all toys had to be hand made. People got married from the tunnels. One couple suffered an air raid in the middle of their wedding service. They had to go back down the tunnels and then finish the service when the raid was over.

### Were there amusing incidents?

One in particular. The only transport in the tunnels was a plate layer's trolley which was formerly used by workmen repairing broken plates that joined lines together on the miniature railways. In the night someone would push this trolley along the lines and then let it go. We wondered what was coming. It made a dreadful creaking and cranking. Nobody could stop it until it got to the end of the line. Soldiers on leave who were sheltering in the tunnels were great jokers and would often be responsible for the trolley's late night run.

### What was the mood of people in the tunnels?

It was a very happy atmosphere. We all looked out for each other. We shared happy news and we shared each other's sorrows – if anyone lost their home or a member of their family. There was no bickering, we all got on with each other You had to do that or you'd go under. We were safe down there though, we knew nothing could penetrate. We'd hold dances and concert parties to keep our spirits up.

### When did you leave the tunnels?

From August 1940 till late 1941 or early 1942, we'd often go for two or three weeks without seeing daylight. We couldn't go up top because the warden would send us back down as the air raids were too bad. Eventually it was decided that we shouldn't be living down there completely and we had to come up during the day. But if there was a raid we got back down there really quickly.

Brian Moses

# Air raid on Guernsey

The Germans bombed Guernsey on the day before they invaded the island in 1940. In Tomorrow is a Stranger by Geoffrey Trease, two children, Paul and Tessa, are caught up in the raid on St Peter Port.

Paul and Tessa turned homewards up the High Street. It was at that moment that the war – for them – began in earnest.

It was just like the films.

Out of the placid evening sky the planes came screeching down over housetops and harbour. Machine-guns rattled. Streams of bullets drew splintered lines across walls. Windows shattered into sprays of murderous fragments.

A scream of terror died on Tessa's lips as Paul grabbed her, hurling them both into an alley. They nearly fell down the shadowy steps that led to the quayside. Instead, they clung to each other under the archway.

They could hear footsteps running in panic along the street, shouted orders, cries and moans. Then the planes swept back, low, deafeningly low, guns blazing. From a distance came the crump of bombs, the delayed crash of a collapsing building, the slow slide of chinking rubble like shingle on the beach.

'How are we going to get *home*?' she wailed.

Paul was wondering too. Later he admitted to her that he'd kept saying to himself, 'Mum will be so *mad* if I'm stupid and get killed.' Funny, really. But not at the time. Not funny at all.

Again that fiendish roar of swooping aircraft. Again the rat-ta-tat of machine-guns, the whine and thump of bombs. They'd be mad to risk the High Street. It stretched through the town-centre, a conspicuous guideline for low-flying pilots. The Nazis could *fillet* St Peter Port, taking it out like the backbone of a fish.

Somehow, though, they must get home. Their parents would be

worried sick. Also – the ghastly realisation dawned on him – the raid wasn't happening only here. All the more reason to get home and make sure that everybody there was all right.

'Better go down here,' he grunted.

They turned from the death-trap of the High Street and went down the dank stone steps. But coming out into the evening brightness of the waterfront they saw that they had exchanged the frying-pan for the fire.

Quite literally fire. Manes of crackling orange flame, flaring skywards into clouds of stinking grey smoke.

The very road was ablaze. The raiders had traversed the line of stationary lorries, pumping bullets into them at close range. Petrol had gushed from the perforated fuel-tanks, washed across the road and exploded into flame.

The harbourside warehouses were built over arcaded passageways. Paul seized Tessa's hand and raced her along under this partial protection. Then a new horror met their eyes. It seemed that the roadway was a mass of blood and – an unthinkable pulp, wet and vivid red.

Tessa let out a choking laugh. 'It's only tomatoes!'

So it was, mostly. A bomb had exploded amid hundreds of crates of the ripe produce.

They ran on, lungs bursting, into another scene of chaos. The farm animals just landed from Alderney had stampeded at the gunfire. They were plunging and rearing madly all over the road. There was a new danger, of getting kicked or gored or crushed against a wall. 'Up here!' he yelled, and hustled her up a side-turning back into the town.

It was quieter there now. They could make for home, zig-zagging through the byways. Glancing back over the rooftops they could see a vast pall of smoke rolling up from the harbour.

Both were welcomed with immense relief when they arrived – and their own relief was no less to find their houses intact and their families unharmed.

Tessa's father, at the first alarm, had seized steel helmet and gasmask and rushed off to his post. It was midnight when he returned, but Tessa was still downstairs. Who could go to bed on such a night? She heard him say wearily, as her mother made yet another pot of tea: 'Twenty fatal casualties, Milly – so far. It'll be more when we get the full list.'

Paul found even Gran downstairs, where she hadn't been for ages. Dad had insisted. No one, he said firmly, was going to stay upstairs tonight. They'd made up a bed for her in the living-room. She was rather enjoying being at the centre of life again.

They switched on the BBC News. Not a word about the raid – *their* raid. Only an official announcement that the Channel Islands had been declared 'open cities'.

'Cities?' said Gran. 'We're not cities.'

'It's just the word they use,' Dad explained patiently. 'Usually it *is* for cities – like Paris the other day. The point is, they're not being defended, they're not military objectives, so there's no excuse for bombing them.'

'H'm,' said Gran disgustedly. 'They might have mentioned that to Hitler a bit sooner.'

From Tomorrow is a Stranger by Geoffrey Trease

# Village shop

A village shop window, stuffed full, with nothing costing more than a penny (you could ask for a penn'orth of anything) is a sight no child can pass. The children of Pakefield were poor. A penny to spend was a rare treat. The spending required a lot of thought and took a lot of time. The penny was spent many times over in the imagination as they peered over the boxes of veg outside the shop at the rows of glass jars at the back of the window.

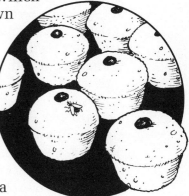

Pear drops, humbugs, fruit drops, liquorice comforts, gob-stoppers. You got more pear drops for a penny, but you might have to share them with your little brother or sister, or any of the notorious *Botwright* brothers if you happened to meet one in a back opening. Gob-stoppers last longer and you were less likely to have to share (although half-sucked gob-stoppers were often passed round, usually from my pocket and then mouth to mouth through the Botwright hierarchy).

Liquorice comforts were most fun. They were sucked slowly until only the black centre remained. This stained all your teeth black. If you were careful you could blacken only a few, or every other one. Earlier in the sucking stage, while there was still colour on the comforts, you could war-paint yourself and several other members of the gang in the full range of candy colours. Psychedelia came early to the Hill Green Gang.

Now, it was my good fortune, as a toddler, to be placed in the middle of this Aladdin's Cave of penny treasures. The only place safe from the feet of busmen and the Allies, and where my mother could keep an eye on me, was in the shop window. Also, away from the dark threat of their skirts, I was less likely to be rude to old ladies.

This was my window on the world. A window criss-crossed with anti-blast sticky tape, but a window which burnt penny-sized holes in the pockets of children in the street. A window past which swirled the machinery of war, the baker's horse-drawn van, the brewers' drays, and Stewey White, the tipsy coalman whose horse took him home every night.

Every ten minutes or so a bus crew would arrive for their five-minute tea break. They liked it 'hot 'n' strong'.

At one end of the glass counter was a big wooden bakers' tray, full of very dull-looking cakes. Some had a fingerprint of jam on top to suggest memories of a cherry. Others had a little black currant on top. If you saw a cake with two currants, one of them would be a fly.

Sitting in the shop window in summer was not without danger. Any bruised fruit attracted swarms of wasps. The wasps would gorge themselves for a while, then climb with sticky feet part way up the window and doze off in the sun. Boys outside the window would pretend to lick them off, or drum on the glass with their fingers and stir the wasps up into such a fury that they would dive-bomb the closely packed tea-swilling customers.

I don't think I was ever stung, despite having the stickiest face and fingers in the village.

*From War Boy: A Country Childhood by Michael Foreman*

# Nadia Cattouse

*During World War II, when many men left their work to enlist in the services, women were encouraged to fill job vacancies for the good of the war effort. Some women came to Britain from Commonwealth countries. Nadia Cattouse came from the Caribbean colony of Belize. She spent two and a half years in the ATS (The Auxiliary Territorial Service).*

From the early 1940s other male members of my family had been leaving Belize. I had an uncle in a forestry unit and cousins in the airforce. In 1943 they eventually asked for volunteers for the ATS. I heard it on the local news at twelve o'clock, and was so eager I jumped on my bike straight away to get to the Drill Hall ... After a series of medicals and interviews I heard I was one of the first six chosen, I left on a boat for Jamaica in November 1943, where we joined a Jamaican contingent and did six months' basic training. We then left for Britain via the United States. I encountered segregation for the first time when we set foot in Miami. The hotel, booked for us by officials in Jamaica, refused to take us, and we were transferred to another hotel on condition we used the back, elevator, entrance. We were angry, upset and surprised but by the time of the train from Miami to New York we had become very determined girls indeed. Wearing our uniforms with British Honduras shoulder flashes we took our seats normally on the train, although black people were not supposed to do this. When the ticket collector came, we refused to compromise, and helped by a Scottish ATS Officer we insisted we would only move if we were given first-class seats. Eventually officials let us travel in a Pullman coach with luxurious pull-down beds.

We arrived in Britain on a ship packed with US servicemen. I can remember my first impressions of London were in the middle of an air-raid, I couldn't understand how everyone was being so cool about it.

Eventually I went to Edinburgh for special training as a signals operator. We worked in shifts sending and receiving messages by Morse key and radio telephones. I was also a part-time PT (physical training) instructor with the ATS.

*From Keep Smiling Through – Women in the Second World War by Caroline Lang*

# Did you know?

Did you know you could:–
Run a car with a gas balloon
Make omelettes with powder
Play houses under a table
Go without sweets
Light a room with gas
Wash with a cold tap
Keep warm with a shovel full of coal
Have kippers as a treat
Not know what a banana was?
Most people had:–
No cars
Varnished floors and lino
No fridges
No bathrooms
No central heating
No television
Did you know:-
There were British Restaurants (sugar spoons chained to the
counters).
No MacDonalds!
There was Woolton Pie, Snook, whalemeat but no Burgers.
Vegetables were home grown, life wriggled happily in each leaf fold.
You washed clothes with Rinso, Persil and great green
squares of Fairy Soap.
Soda stripped the hands raw when meal-time washing up was done.
Radios were bakelite with great glass valves inside them.
Battery run, water filled, we heaved them from the refilling shop.
People used buses with a conductor and a driver.
Trains ran on steam dirtying hands and filling eyes with cinders.
Toys made with celluloid, no plastics yet, caught fire easily
with a spark from Dad's Woodbine.
Whips and tops, cowboys and indians, playground chants filled
the time.
We grouped as gangs, not playing alone with electronic toys.
Crisps had blue bags of salt in them.
Sucking them happily we drank gallons of Tizer.
Most old people say:–
Those were the good old days.
WHAT DO YOU THINK?

Karlen Lawrence

# 'The King is dead'

'Tell your mother the king is dead.'

It was February 6th, 1952 and I was only seven years old – but I can remember the occasion as if it were yesterday.

I was coming home from school, walking up Blackstock Road and approaching Highbury Barn. I usually liked school but it had been a boring sort of day. The most momentous thing that had happened was I'd tried to do a headstand against the playground wall but had failed as usual – and I had slipped and grazed my knee. The school secretary had dabbed it with iodine and it had stung so much that my eyes had filled with tears – but I hadn't cried. If I hadn't cried from the pain caused by a grazed knee then I'm afraid I wasn't likely to cry for the dead king. (He'd looked very old in the photographs anyway – at least twenty.)

My primary school was in a street very near the Arsenal football stadium and once when they had a midweek match the whole school had been given a half-day holiday so that we were safely home before the crowds of supporters arrived. I thought I was going to like the Arsenal – but that half-day holiday only happened once.

The teachers at my school were friendly and caring and I remember it as a very happy place. Although the Second World War had been over almost seven years, there were not many luxuries around. In those days, simple things seemed very important. I remember that the previous December we had made miniature Christmas trees from white pipe cleaners that our teacher had bought from Woolworth's and we had draped them with strands of silver tinsel, then stuck them in egg cups filled with earth and cotton wool. When I look back to that time, I realise that they probably just looked like white pipe cleaners draped with silver tinsel – but to me they were magical. If I close my eyes, I can still imagine the small table in the darkened school corridor, completely covered with forty Christmas trees all glistening with 'snow'.

On my way home, up the hill past St John's Church and towards Highbury Barn, I would often call in at the newsagent and sweetshop for a penny liquorice ring, a sherbet dab or a round ball of bubblegum that changed colours when you sucked at it. Once a week, I would also buy my copy of the *Beano* and *Dandy* (later to be replaced by *The Eagle* and Dan Dare's space-age struggles against the Mekon), for the latest exploits of Dennis the Menace or the trials and tribulations of Keyhole Kate.

It was when I emerged from the shop on February 6th 1952 that I was given my all-important message: 'Tell your mother that the king is dead', the lady told me. I'm sure I had never seen her before in my life, and to this day I don't know who she was. But I can remember feeling a sense of complete and utter shock. Not, I'm afraid, because King George VI (our present Queen Elizabeth's father) was dead; but because, until that *precise* moment, I hadn't realised we were on such *intimate* terms with him!

'Fancy, knowing the *king*,' I thought! For why else would the lady have told me to give my mother such an important message?

I can remember feeling slightly perplexed when, having told her the news, my mother seemed more interested in wringing out the washing at that precise moment ... History is funny like that.

Trevor Harvey

# The Coronation

I was eight years old in 1953 when our Queen was crowned. This took place at a big church in London called Westminster Abbey.

In those days television was new. Our TV was the only one in the street. It had a screen the size of a small book, and was set in a big wooden box that stood on the floor. To make the screen a bit bigger we had a magnifying glass fixed to it. The picture was fuzzy black and white. It was like looking into a goldfish bowl.

All the neighbours came to our house to watch the Coronation. You had to be in the front row to see very much. Little ones like me lay on the floor.

We watched Elizabeth ride to the Abbey in her golden coach. We saw the Archbishop place the crown on her head. We listened as she promised to serve her country. That was when Elizabeth became Her Majesty the Queen.

The schools were closed that day. Everybody was on holiday. The grown-ups drank a lot of beer and got very silly. The children went to parties in the street. Ours was paid for by the richest man in town. I don't know his name, but his food was very good.

At the end of the day we were given a silver spoon, a plate, and a cup and saucer. Each one was decorated with the royal coat of arms. I lost mine years ago. I wish I had taken better care of them.

Alan Brown

# 1950s Schooldays

Every morning school started with us being tested on our spellings and our tables. Then there was a general knowledge test. Mark Hall was a technical modern so it was considered inferior to the grammar school. You only went to the grammar school if you'd passed the 11-plus exam. Most of the teachers were men as women only taught cookery, needlework, P.E. and French. Boys did woodwork and metalwork, girls did needlework and cooking. For P.E. and games boys and girls were strictly separate. Even if the hockey pitch touched the soccer pitch we weren't allowed to say 'hello' to the boys.

Sport was a very big part of school life. I was quite good at athletics and rounders. My friend Ann and I were always about equal. Sometimes I came first, sometimes she did.

We were certainly no angels by the time we reached Mark Hall. On the last day of term we used to stuff newspaper up the exhaust pipe of the teachers' cars. Not many of them had cars but the physics teacher had a Ford Popular. We used to stand at the bus stop and hope he'd give us a lift.

The punishment for bad behaviour at school was being kept in and made to write lines, or sometimes you got a sharp rap on the knuckles with a ruler. One of the boys in my class was slippered by the religious education teacher for making a mess on the floor with chalk during a wet breaktime. If we got into trouble at school we never told our parents.

We spent ages practising with our hula-hoops, during break-times and when we got home. The idea was to keep them going for as long as possible. You had to wiggle your hips very fast to keep the hoop from falling down. I wasn't bad at that. Ann wasn't so good because she never had much of a waist.

From When I was Young: The Fifties by Neil Thompson and Pat Scott

# Teds

Teddy Boys first appeared in Britain in the early 1950s, along with skiffle groups and rock 'n' roll. They got their name from the Edwardian style of their clothes – long jacket, narrow trousers, white shirt (never a striped one), narrow bow tie. Shoes were usually suede with thick soles or leather with long thin points – winklepickers. Hair was set in quiffs with long sideboards. Most men's barbers only did traditional 'short back and sides' haircuts so hair could be a real problem.

Occasionally there would be fights between rival gangs and sometimes knives were used but Teddy Boys were not as dangerous as many adults seemed to think. They were just different.

They always hung around in the same place. In the park, by the big elm tree. They were there most weathers. If it was wet they would huddle beneath its spreading branches. On sunny days they sprawled along the benches, daring anyone to sit there.

No one did. Us kids walked a little faster when the teddy boys were in the park. If they caught one of us staring they would call out,

'Wotchoolookinat?'

Sometimes they even talked like this to adults.

If a girl walked by they would whistle. Once they whistled at my sister when we were walking back from the shops together. We ran all the way home.

'You keep away from them,' my mum warned us. 'They've got flick knives and winklepickers and they use bad language.'

Wotchoolookinatmate.

I had no idea what winklepickers were. They sounded a lot worse than flick knives or bad language.

My mum also said that if I didn't work hard at school I would end up a teddy boy too. That worried me a lot.

They frightened me. But they fascinated me too. I would watch them sometimes, out of the corner of my eye. They wore string ties and tight trousers. They had weird hairstyles and bright coloured jackets that reached to their knees. Watching them prowl about the elm tree was like watching strange new arrivals at the zoo. Dangerous ones too if they caught you staring.

Wotchoolookinaten?

But I never saw them do any harm.

Until one Saturday.

Tony and I were walking home through the park after Saturday morning pictures. Tony was my best mate. He also lived two doors down from me, which was handy for a best mate.

We'd spent all our money – one and a tanner to get in plus another tanner for sweets – but it had been a good show so we didn't care. We wouldn't have cared if it had been a bad show. We didn't go to Saturday morning pictures just to see the films. We went to boo the baddies on the screen, throw our empty sweet wrappers at the smaller kids and cheek the usherettes as they waved their torches along the rows.

We had done all of these so we were feeling pretty pleased with ourselves.

Then we came to the elm tree.

There were four of them today. As we walked by we could feel their eyes following us. I just looked straight ahead but Tony suddenly lowered his face and started walking faster, almost running. He looked really worried.

'Oh no,' I heard him mutter.

'It's all right," I said. I hurried to catch up. 'They never do anything. Just don't look.'

'Oi!' a voice called out. That did make me look.

I couldn't believe it. One of them was coming after us. What had we done?

'Oi!' His red jacket flapped like wings. His trousers were so tight they made his legs look like sticks as he ran jerking towards us.

But I didn't laugh. I wanted to run. I didn't want to be the first to run though. Tony was older than me. I waited for him to make the first move. If we made a dash for it now we might make it. The end of the park wasn't far away. I felt that once we were in our street, surrounded by houses, we would be safe.

But Tony didn't run. For a moment he looked as if he was thinking about it. then he just gave a sigh and slowed down. The teddy boy's hand grabbed his collar.

I stopped too. I stared up at a bony face covered in spots. I was close enough to smell the cream in his hair. I had never been this close to a teddy boy before. I couldn't help staring.

His dark hair hung over his forehead like the peak of a rather floppy cap. His sideboards were so straight they looked as if they'd been glued

on. Inside his jacket was a blue lining that shimmered like silk. His shirt had the sort of whiteness that the adverts on the telly were always promising.

I thought, All that gear, it must have cost a fiver at least.

Then I thought, I know that face.

I waited for him to turn round and threaten me with a flick knife or a winklepicker, but he was too busy shaking Tony to notice me.

'Where's my fags then?'

Tony shook himself free. 'I forgot to get them, all right? Sorry.' He tried to shrug his collar back into shape. He didn't look at me.

'I dunno. I can't trust you with nothing, can I?' He turned to me. 'Wotcher, Pete.'

'Hello, Eric,' I mumbled. I was still a bit shocked. I hadn't seen Tony's big brother for months, not since he was doing his O Levels. He hadn't been a teddy boy then. But lately when I called for Tony I would sometimes hear music playing upstairs. I recognised some of it too. Elvis Presley. Elvis the Pelvis my dad called him.

Eric had changed a lot in six months. Was it because he had stopped working hard at school?

He was talking to me. 'Here's half a crown I said. Get me ten Woodbine and keep the change. You think he'd be pleased to do a little job like that, wouldn't you?'

I nodded frantically.

Tony was starting to walk off. He wasn't looking scared any more. Just annoyed and a bit embarrassed. Like someone whose well-kept secret is out at last.

'Oi!'

Eric grabbed him again. By the arm this time. 'Where's my half a dollar then?'

Tony silently handed him the silver coin.

As we walked away I sneaked a backward glance. I still half expected to be threatened but Eric just waved cheerily.

'See you, Pete.'

I said to Tony, 'Your brother's changed a lot since I last saw him.'

'Yeh.' He sounded as if he didn't want to talk about it.

'What do your mum and dad think?'

'They don't like to talk about it.'

I glanced around again. Eric had rejoined his friends under the tree. They were whistling at two girls who were walking by. The girls giggled shyly and walked a bit faster.

'They say it's just a phase he's going through,' Tony said. 'He'll get over it soon.'

The faster the girls walked the louder the teddy boys whistled. Eric was whistling too. His thin spotty face was alight. His mouth was a grinning black hole. 'Ello Darlin!' he yelled.

I looked at Tony. He was trying hard not to smile.

'I hope they're right,' I said.

We ran home, laughing all the way.

Peter Hanratty

# Be there or be square

My first introduction to music was by means of a wind up gramophone and a collection of 78 rpm records. They always crackled and if I forgot to turn the handle the music slowed and then came to a halt as the turntable stopped revolving.

Later on I bought a tiny transistor radio, a 'trannie', and on Sunday afternoon walks I'd hold it to my ear and listen in to 'Pick of the Pops' with disc jockey Alan Freeman. At night I'd tune in to Radio Luxembourg. The reception was terrible but drifting in and out of the crackles, whines and hums I caught snatches of wonderful rock and roll tunes.

I was twelve when I first heard the Beatles being played. 'Love Me Do' was a simple enough song but the combination of hoarse vocals, electric guitar and wailing harmonica had me hooked. But who was producing this wonderful noise? The New Musical Express filled me in on the details. Four lads from Liverpool – John Lennon (The raw voice on 'Love Me Do'), Paul McCartney, George Harrison and Ringo Starr. Their photographs showed that they had long hair, not the normal short back and sides cut.

When their second record appeared in early 1963, it stormed up the charts to number 2. I saw the Beatles on television. My father didn't approve. 'They need a haircut,' he announced. Records were six shillings (30p) or thereabouts. I bought a copy and played it again and again.

As the year went on, the Beatles became big news, really big news. Each record went straight to the top of the charts and the fans at their live shows went crazy. The press coined a new word to describe what was happening, 'Beatlemania'.

Towards Christmas I learnt that on their new tour the Beatles would be visiting my home town. Tickets were to go on sale one Saturday morning at 10 o'clock. My friend Richard arranged to join me in the queue for tickets, a couple of hours or so before the box office opened.

When we arrived we couldn't believe our eyes. The queue stretched all round the theatre, along the main road and down a side street. Those at the front had been queuing all night, they'd brought sleeping bags, and thermos flasks, some had found deck chairs to sit in, others just sprawled across the pavement. The police were there to direct traffic or perhaps they were anticipating trouble when vast numbers of young people were turned away without tickets. We stayed in the queue, shuffling along for most of the morning until finally our patience was rewarded.

On the night of the performance I wore my black winklepickers – tight shoes with pointed toes. I swore to my parents that they were comfortable but the price of being fashionable was pinched toes and a peculiar way of walking. The Beatles were part of a package show and we sat through several acts before our idols finally appeared. Then the noise which had been growing all evening finally erupted into a huge wall of sound. We didn't hear anything that was played because of all the screaming and shouting and weeping that went on all around us. But we were there and 'being there' was what it was all about in the sixties.

And then our parents started to like the Beatles and it was as if they didn't belong to us any more. I found new idols – The Animals, The Who, The Kinks. Hair was worn longer, songs were wilder and more bluesy, and there was little chance that adults would find them attractive. Friday evenings found me in front of the television for an hour of 'Ready, Steady, Go!' 'The Weekend Starts Here' they told us, and in grainy black and white I watched the real bad boys of rock and roll, The Rolling Stones.

Soon we had twenty-four hour a day pop music blasted out from pirate radio ships which were anchored in the North Sea. Radio Caroline set the trend, followed by Radio London. Other stations broadcast from wartime forts in the Thames Estuary. I tuned in all the time, turned the dial to high and learned a whole new language. Everything was suddenly 'fab', 'gear' or 'groovy'. My homework suffered but I thought I'd discovered a purpose to life.

'Dad.' I asked, 'Would you buy me a guitar?'

Brian Moses

# Colonisation in reverse

After World War II there was a huge increase in immigration to Britain from British Commonwealth countries. People born in those countries that previously formed the British Empire were legally entitled to live in Britain. Many people were encouraged to emigrate to Britain by the promise of jobs in the hotel industry and in London Transport. A large proportion of immigrants came from the West Indies. 'Colonisation in reverse' refers to the fact that European settlers first went to the West Indies in previous centuries and settled there in great numbers. Now the flow was in the opposite direction.

What a joyful news Miss Mattie,
I feel like me heart gwine burs.
Jamaica people colonizin
Englan in reverse.

By de hundred, by de t'ousan
From country and from town
By de ship load, by de plane load
Jamaica is Englan boun.

Dem a pour out o'Jamaica
Everybody future plan
Is fe get a big time job
An settle in de mother lan...

From Time Detectives: Elizabeth's story by Louise Bennett

# No dogs, children or Coloureds

The year is 1958 and the Vincent family are among the first immigrants to arrive in Britain from Jamaica. Jonas has been offered a job on the buses and is optimistic about England. His wife Ella, and older children Wellington and Nelson are apprehensive. The first hurdle they must face is to find accommodation but many landlords are hostile to immigrants.

They found the street and the house without difficulty. Jonas climbed the steps and rang the bell and an enormous lady with bright yellow hair opened the door.

'We 'aven't got any,' she said before Jonas had a chance to speak.

'I beg your pardon?'

'Rooms. That's what you've come about, innit?'

'Well yes, you see my friend gave me ...'

'Well 'e shouldn't 'ave done.'

'I'm sorry,' said Jonas. 'I must have taken it down wrong. I'm sorry to have troubled you.'

He turned to go.

'I'm not having none of you lot here!' she called after him and disappeared inside, slamming the door behind her.

'What did she mean by "us lot", pappa?' asked Nelson. 'She doesn't know us, does she?'

'I don't know, son. Never mind. We're bound to find somewhere soon.' Nelson looked up and down the street. Tall, forbidding houses, three storeys above the road and one below, each one the same as its neighbour, with steps leading up to the front door. Ugly metal stumps surrounded the basement area.

'What are those?' he asked.

'They're the remains of railings. They took them in the war because they needed the metal to make guns.'

'Oh.' Nelson was silent for a moment. 'Why aren't there any trees or gardens?'

'They're probably in some other part.'

The family walked on up the road, passing a large bomb site. Weeds and grasses had grown among the rubble and when Nelson looked up he could see half a room that was still attached to the house next door, its wallpaper faded but intact.

'Why don't they clear the mess away, pappa?'

'Too many bombs fell for them all to be cleared at once.'

Nelson digested this in silence and the family turned a corner and started walking up another long street, identical to the one they had just left.

'Where we going to stay tonight, pappa?' Jonas did not speak.

'What about Mr King, pappa? He's living over here, isn't he? Couldn't we go stay with him?'

'He's moved out of London, boy.'

'Where's he moved to, pappa?' Nelson asked, trying to keep his mind away from the depressing effect of the dreary streets and the increasing heaviness of the suitcases he carried.

'He's gone to a town called Nottingham,' Ella answered.

'Can't we go there too?'

'You ask too many questions, boy,' Jonas said with a frown.

'Yeah,' said Wellington. 'Hush your face.'

Ella sighed and shifted baby Winston to a more comfortable position.

'I got other addresses, Ella. Don't you worry. I spent some time before we left making a list of addresses. Look, there's one here.'

They stopped outside a house and Jonas ran up the steps. A large notice was pinned to the door:

ROOMS TO LET

Underneath was written:

NO DOGS, CHILDREN OR COLOUREDS

Despite the notice, Jonas rang the bell. After a while a man appeared. 'Yes?'

'I'm looking for accommodation for myself and my family. I understand ...'

'Can't you folks read?' the man interrupted. 'You're the third lot today.' He pointed to the notice and read it out slowly and deliberately.

' "No dogs, children or coloureds". Don't suppose any of you can read, place you've come from.'

'I can read, sir, but I thought...'

'Well you thought wrong, mister. No children or coloureds.'

The afternoon wore drearily away. The cases Nelson carried seemed to get heavier and heavier with every door that was slammed in their faces. Wellington started whistling through his teeth, a hard, angry look in his eyes, and baby Winston began to cry. Even Jonas walked more slowly, the spring gone from his step.

'The baby's hungry, Jonas.'

'We're all hungry, woman,' Jonas snapped in uncustomary anger.

Nelson spoke for them all. 'Why don't they want us, pappa?'

Jonas did not reply.

The last house on Jonas' list was at the bottom of a cul-de-sac adjoining

the railway line. A large brick wall cut the street off from the railway and two boys about Nelson's age were throwing a ball against it. They stopped their game and turned to watch as the family paused outside the house. Once again Jonas mounted the steps.

He was a long time talking to the middle-aged man who appeared at the door. The man was only partly dressed – grubby trousers held up by braces over a dirty vest. The smell of rotting vegetables wafted down the steps and Nelson wrinkled his nose. Despite his tiredness he hoped that the man would send them away.

But the man was nodding and there was Jonas, bounding down the steps, face beaming, good humour fully restored.

'I told you it would be all right, didn't I? Trust in the Lord and He will provide. Come on – come on – the room's this way...'

He led the way down crumbling steps into the basement. The man reappeared at the basement door and ushered them in.

'Your own front door so you can come and go as you please,' he said, as they filed past him. The hallway was dark, with peeling wallpaper.

The man opened the nearest door with a flourish.

'And 'ere's your new 'ome. 'Ome from 'ome, you might say. All mod. cons. and no expense spared for our overseas guests, and at three quid a week, cheap as anywhere you'll get in London. Payment a month in advance if you don't mind, Mr...er...?'

'Vincent. Jonas Vincent.'

'Mine's Slater. Jim Slater. Pleased t'er make your acquaintance. This your wife and nippers?'

'My wife and children, yes.'

Mr Slater winked broadly. 'Only brought one wife I see – left the others back 'ome, eh?'

'I only have one wife.'

'Well, I know your sort, but I'm broadminded. And nippers too. I like nippers, though there's some round 'ere won't take 'em. But I reckon it's security, if you take my meaning. Less likely to scarper if you've kids to support, eh?'

Jonas laughed politely with Mr Slater, and Nelson, too, grinned nervously, although neither of them understood what Mr Slater meant. Wellington raised one eyebrow and leaned against the wall, and Ella looked helplessly at Jonas. Mr Slater caught the look.

'I can see what your good lady's thinkin',' he said. 'She's wonderin' where she's to do 'er cookin' and such. One-track minds, the ladies, God bless 'em. 'Ere we are then, through 'ere's the scullery. Bit small, I grant you, but compact an' everything you need. The toilet's on the landing. You share that with another family, but you won't mind that, will you? Luxury itself, I bet, considerin' where you come from.'

He led the way back into the main room.

'Where do we sleep?' hissed Nelson.

Mr Slater overheard and the welcoming smile went from his face as quickly as if a duster had been wiped over it.

'Sleep? You sleep in 'ere of course. What else do you expect for three quid a week – a four-bedroomed 'ouse in Wembley? Of course, if it's not good enough for you guv...'

'Thank you. We'll take it,' Jonas said.

Mr Slater relaxed and the smile returned.

'I should think so. You won't find a lot of places round here takin' your sort, you know. Had a lot of trouble with darkies, one way and another. Not everyone's as tolerant as me and the missis.'

'We're very grateful,' said Jonas.

'All right then. Perhaps you and me could settle up...?' Mr Slater suggested, and he and Jonas went out.

The room seemed very quiet and still. Nelson looked round. It was a small room with dingy wallpaper, peeling here and there near the ceiling. It was also dark, as the window gave on to a tiny enclosed yard, sealed in at pavement level by metal bars. The window, too, was barred with metal spikes.

'They didn't take the metal here for the war,' Nelson said.

Wellington strolled over to a switch and turned on the light. A single naked bulb shed a dim glow, highlighting the drabness of the place. Two double beds took up most of the space, and the remainder of the room was crammed with a cheap utility table, four chairs, a brown sofa that had seen better days, and a small gas fire set into the wall. The floor was covered with dirty green linoleum.

Ella laid Winston down on one of the beds and went into the scullery. Nelson followed her into an area little more than a cupboard. It had an old gas stove, a cracked enamel sink with one cold tap, and a small work-space with shelves underneath. The walls had been painted with yellow gloss paint, now bubbling and peeling. Behind the stove, a greyish fungus spread up from the skirting board. Ella sighed and went back into the main room as Jonas re-entered from the hall.

'Well, what you think? It's all right, isn't it?'

'It's very dirty,' Ella said.

'Dirt? What's a bit of dirt? We'll soon clean it up. Two beds, eh? That's good. Bedding, too, thrown in with the rent. We could have done a lot worse.'

'If you say so.'

'Of course I say so. You're just tired, that's all. And hungry too. I expect you boys are hungry, aren't you?'

'Yes, pappa.'

'Right … right. We'll see about some food.'

And Jonas smiled at his family, a smile that, unlike Mr Slater's came straight from the heart. 'We're home, Ella … boys. We're home.'

*From Milk and Honey by Avril Rowlands*

# The journey I will never forget

Following the Vietnam War, North and South Vietnam were united under a Communist government in 1976. Over the next few years, thousands of refugees fled Vietnam as the government tried to get rid of what they called 'undesirables'. Many of these people were of Chinese origin and China had long been an enemy of Vietnam. Others were middle-class residents although some were peasants and fishermen. Many of the refugees left in small boats trying to reach Malaysia or Hong Kong. Large numbers of these 'boat people' were drowned at sea, or starved to death or were killed by pirates. However, many survived the long journeys and neighbouring countries couldn't cope with the sudden increase in population. The United Nations helped by finding homes for these refugees in many countries around the world.
This is the story of Tran Dang and her family as told to her teacher, a few weeks after her arrival in Britain.

I lived in Vietnam and my name is Tran. I am ten years old. I shall try to tell you how I came to leave my country and why it was necessary to do so.

The story begins with my grandfather who was a good doctor but Chinese not Vietnamese. He had plenty of money and bought his food from Chinese shops. He treated his patients well and they paid him, not in money, but in goods or things they could catch, like fish or chickens which they kept.

My father also had some medical knowledge and would help people. There were many injuries through sport or through carelessness. My father was only sixteen. Some people were grateful for what they did but others were envious particularly of the lovely house we lived in, set in a garden with a separate cooking house, separate toilet outside. The house had two large downstairs living rooms, one for our family, which was mother, father, three girls and one brother Tuong. My grandmother died very young but grandfather and my father kept a room of remembrance for them where there was a picture of her.

One day the police came to our house and we were ordered to form two groups in the town square. My sisters already had been bullied at school by older girls. In one group stood the Vietnamese and in the other ourselves, the Vietnam/Chinese, of which there were about twenty to forty people. They asked, would we like to stay in the country as servants and be housed in poor farms and grow crops? We would have to live off the land with no money or we could leave the country completely. Some of the Chinese/Vietnamese were sent immediately to far off farms. The Vietnamese took immediate possession. My father, together with the other Chinese and Vietnamese, who did not want to live in a country where there was always fighting, decided to get together, pool their money and buy a boat.

Terrible things were happening all around, Chinese burning down Vietnamese villages and confusion reigned everywhere. We prepared to get on board the boat. All was left behind but the little money we had after buying the boat was hidden all over our clothes, in our hems, cuffs, in collars, under hats and all we carried were pots and pans used for eating rice. The boat lay at anchor not far away and was large, brown and white.

The sea that day looked rough and as we approached ready to board many were crying, men and women. My mother and my two sisters were crying and said that they could not come with us as she was Vietnamese and could not face the stormy sea and leave her home country. I embraced them for the last time and we stood on the deck waving goodbye until they were just little dots. It was very sad.

My father took charge of the organisation on the boat. He knew which men he could trust to help him. Even so there was fighting because, at times, there was not sufficient food. It had been decided that the captain and crew should have special treatment and have the best food, but the rest of the passengers should do with as little as possible. For a week our three had to make do with one cupful of rice each and for drinking, the horrible brown water was served in cups. The mothers with babies were not able to feed them, but the new born baby (and there was only one) survived and was a sturdy baby.

About the third day there was a dreadful shock in store for us. We were hit by a freak wave which whirled the boat round and broke the anchor and flung people to the deck. All were seasick and could not keep to their feet. There was vomit everywhere, even on my skirt. Mothers could not help being sick over their children. The wind and rain beat down on us. Women were praying. Next we struck rocks and a hole appeared in the front of the boat. People were soon in the front of the boat. People stripped off their coats and blankets to soak up the water. That left them nothing to protect themselves against the weather.

This foul weather continued for a day but the boat was saved and stayed afloat. At last we saw the sun. We had been in our cabins sitting on the floor trying to rest for we had no hammocks. In the end, the boat was driven towards a lighthouse manned by a Chinaman. He came down to us and helped us over the rocks and towards the land.

After walking about an hour in the wind and rain over hard rocks we finally came to a building which we entered but which only protected us from the wind. Here we lit a fire made of dried leaves and branches and finally we felt warm. There were Chinese people already there who gave us biscuits, very dry, but we were so hungry we ate them gladly.

Next day, the Chinese who befriended us accompanied us in sunshine back to the boat for they wanted to buy from us watches and coats, which they had not seen for sometime. On the same day two fishermen with a small boat said that they could guide us to Hong Kong, but first they must do some fishing. We gave them money for they promised to return and guide us safely to Hong Kong, but they never returned and we never saw our money again either!

We waited all day for the fishermen to return but, despite our disappointment, we had a lovely surprise, for, in the darkness, we suddenly saw lights! Lights! The lights of a big boat and there were people waving, very happy to have found us, for they were from Hong Kong.

Ropes were secured to the prow of our boat and we were pulled off the rocks. A small launch roared into view and the men scrambled on board and asked us many questions and all the passengers were so pleased to see friendly faces again.

We told them of our adventures and our need for food, especially milk for the baby. Back came the boat and with it milk in a bottle for the baby. Each family was given a small bowl of rice which we ate, rationing ourselves to so much for the two days it took to reach Hong Kong.

Hong! Kong! A city of twinkling lights and friendly people. We were taken first to a big house and interviewed by the Press and the Police. That night we were given some reasonable food and water and we slept on the floor. Regrettably the toilet was dirty just as it had been on the boat.

The Police came the next day with water, cold water in which we were allowed to wash ourselves and our clothes taking only one hour in all, so that our clothes were damp when we put them on.

After three days we went to a different house. We had luckily been picked as one of ten families where there was only the father and no wife. The rest remained and spent another two weeks in the first big house.

We spent a month in Hong Kong in four different houses which were quite clean, but where the cooking was very difficult as we had to share with several families and the kitchen was far from where we slept. My father went out to work and I spent my time cooking or stopping Tuong from fighting all the other boys.

Finally, my father told us that we would be going to England (where it would be raining all day we were told but this was not true).

Now, after those many adventures, I live happily in England; for my father was wise and did not listen to people who ran down England. He said England would be a good land in which to settle.

At the end of the flight we landed in a cold, wet place but were given a kind welcome by nurses who checked our hair, teeth, throats and then gave us a good meal. Everyone was very happy and friendly and I thought to myself, 'I think we shall like this England...'

Tran Dang (aided by Mrs Averil Weekes)

# The first men on the Moon, 21 July 1969

Apollo II, carrying Neil Armstrong, Lieutenant-Colonel Michael Collins, and Colonel Edwin Aldrin, was launched on 15 July. At 03.56 BST on 21 July Armstrong stepped off the ladder of lunar landing vehicle Eagle on to the Moon.

**NEIL ARMSTRONG:** The most dramatic recollections I had were the sights themselves. Of all the spectacular views we had, the most impressive to me was on the way to the Moon, when we flew through its shadow. We were still thousands of miles away, but close enough, so that the Moon almost filled our circular window. It was eclipsing the Sun, from our position, and the corona of the Sun was visible around the limb of the Moon as a gigantic lens-shaped or saucer-shaped light, stretching out to several lunar diameters. It was magnificent, but the Moon was even more so. We were in its shadow, so there was no part of it illuminated by the Sun. It was illuminated only by earthshine. It made the Moon appear blue-grey, and the entire scene looked decided three-dimensional.

I was really aware, visually aware, that the Moon was in fact a sphere not a disc. It seemed almost as if it were showing us its roundness, its similarity in shape to our Earth, in a sort of welcome. I was sure that it would be a hospitable host. It had been awaiting its first visitors for a long time...

(*After touchdown*) The sky is black, you know. It's a very dark sky. But it still seemed more like daylight than darkness as we looked out the window. It's a peculiar thing, but the surface looked very warm and inviting. It was the sort of situation in which you felt like going out there in nothing but a swimming suit to get a little sun. From the cockpit, the surface seemed to be tan. It's hard to account for that, because later when I held this material in my hand, it wasn't tan at all. It was black, grey and so on. It's some kind of lighting effect, but out the window the surface looks much more like light desert sand than black sand ....

**EDWIN E. ALDRIN** (*on the moon*): The blue colour of my boot has completely disappeared now into this – still don't know exactly what colour to describe this other than greyish-cocoa colour. It appears to be covering most of the lighter part of my boot ... very fine particles ...

(*Later*) The Moon was a very natural and pleasant environment in which to work. It had many of the advantages of zero gravity, but it was in a sense less lonesome than Zero G, where you always have to pay attention to securing attachment points to give you some means of leverage. In one-sixth gravity, on the Moon, you had a distinct feeling of being somewhere ... As we deployed our experiments on the surface we had to jettison things like lanyards, retaining fasteners, etc., and some of these we tossed away. The objects would go away with a slow, lazy motion. If anyone tried to throw a baseball back and forth in that atmosphere he would have difficulty, at first, acclimatizing himself to that slow, lazy trajectory; but I believe he could adapt to it quite readily ...

Odour is very subjective, but to me there was a distinct smell to the lunar material – pungent, like gunpowder or spent cap-pistol caps.

Neil Armstrong and Edwin E. Aldrin

# Home from the sea

In the twenties, thirties and forties many sailors came from what is today called Bangladesh and settled in Cardiff, London, Liverpool and other port towns. They had sailed in merchant ships all over the world and during the Second World War they risked their lives in helping to transport essential supplies to and from Britain.

The bell is ringing insistently, again and again. There is a banging at the door and the scuttling, scrabbling noise of a key seeking its hole; and all along the noise of panting sobs, breathless and desperate.

Old Ustad Miah had dozed off on the sofa, but suddenly came to life again as his brain registered the commotion outside. Kalpana! he thought with shocking clarity. It could only be her. She had gone to the shops a few minutes ago and no one else was due home for a while still. As quickly as his old legs would carry him he got to the door and unlocked the double locking mechanism. His twelve-year-old youngest granddaughter fell into his arms, her whole body shaking and her large eyes rolling with fear.

He made soothing, crooning noises, 'What's happened, what's happened?' and led her to the sofa where he had been having his peaceful catnap. He sat her down and went back to the front door, opening it cautiously. There was nothing unusual to be seen up and down the street. It was a sunny afternoon and the tall Georgian houses in the East London street looked blankly back. The only sign of disturbance was a packet of Tate and Lyle sugar which had burst and spilled its white contents all over the front doorstep.

Kalpana's cheeks were wet with tears. 'They chased me. All down the street. A gang of boys, six or seven of them. They said they would come and get me. They threw stones and I fell down...'

Ustad Miah wiped her face and comforted her as best he could. There was not much else he could do. He was too old and had seen too much. He couldn't even feel great anger any more at what was happening on the streets of the East End. So different from when he was a young man. It had been a friendlier world then.

\* \* \*

When he had arrived in London's East End in 1944, there were just a few dozen Bengali settlers. They weren't known as Bangladeshis then, since Bangladesh only came into existence some thirty years later. He was a sailor and had decided to jump ship at Cardiff. He had been at sea ever since the war started in 1939 and he had just turned twenty. He did it on

impulse, it wasn't really planned. He had heard from his cousin that there were plenty of jobs to be had in London. He had to make sure that the shipping company wouldn't be able to trace him, so there was an element of risk and daring about his decision. His cousin had sent him a message that once he got to London he would be looked after. 'Why not,' he thought, 'I'll stay for a few months and go back home when the war's over.'

He waited till it was dark and hid behind a lifeboat. When the watchman disappeared for a few minutes he crept down the gangplank of the ship, scaled a wall and scarpered into the night. He only had a pound in his pocket, since sailors were paid at the end of a voyage and he would have been given his money on his return to Calcutta.

Looking for the station in the blackout wasn't easy, but he finally got there and asked for a ticket to London. He had been standing by the ticket office trying to count out the exact fare when three squaddies came up and asked if he needed help. It was like that in Britain then. Everyone was so polite and helpful. 'We'll take you there,' they said when he showed the scrap of paper with his cousin's address. They were going back to the front after some leave and their knapsacks were full of homemade cake and sandwiches. 'Go on, have some,' they offered him sandwiches wrapped in brown paper, but he shook his head. He took a piece of cake though.

When they arrived at Paddington the sirens started, so they ran into the underground. Ustad Miah hadn't been scared at all, he'd seen much worse. All the way back from Australia there had been the threat of German submarines. They'd been in a convoy from Port Said and three ships had been sunk on the way to Cardiff. One of the squaddies pumped his hand. 'Merchant navy, eh? Well you lot've done your bit for the war, so cheers and down with the Jerries!'

\* \* \*

Ustad Miah had been to London once before on an earlier voyage. He stayed for a week before returning to his ship. A little girl walking behind him in the street said loudly, 'Oh look, Mum, a black man!' She'd been smacked for that by her mother, who'd come to him all red-faced with embarrassment and apologised. But he had laughed and not been a bit offended. There were very few dark-skinned people like him in London then and the child had meant no harm.

So different now. Horrible language, filthy words. Poor Kalpana. Very different for her generation. He patted her knee again. 'Cup of tea?' he enquired gently. Oh yes, he could make a good cuppa. He'd learned that on the ships, but he had learned to cook in his second job in London when he was under-cook at The Light of Bengal restaurant in South Kensington. Indian restaurants were few and far between in those days. Their customers were mainly British people who had lived and worked in India, and were used to curries. Jhalfarezi, dal, rice, prawn curry, mixed veg – he could cook all those dishes. It had been hot work in the kitchens, but nothing compared with the engine room of the SS *Clanbrook*. Once he nearly passed out in the heat when they were on their way to Aden. 'Come on, boy!' the chief fireman cried. 'We're tough, we sailors from Bengal!' (It used to be East Bengal in those days.) 'Those white cissies can't take a bit of heat and smoke like us,' and Ustad Miah had gritted his teeth and carried on shovelling coal to get the steam up. It was a hard life but there had been the companionship of friends and what he liked best about being a sailor was going home to his village and telling his stories to an admiring audience. Oh, what a fuss they'd made of him! He felt a real hero then.

It had been good fun sailing from Calcutta to Melbourne, Tokyo, Los Angeles, Cape Town, Marseilles, Genoa, Alexandria, Athens. The ships carried cargoes of wheat, pig iron, cement, phosphates and oil. He'd been nearly everywhere. He liked Africa: Mombassa best of all. Fruit was so cheap – mangoes, bananas, pineapples. You never got to see fruit on the ship. It was dal and rice and meat all the time. All the Indian sailors would eat on deck in the evening when the stars and the moon were out and sometimes, after their meal, they would sing a song or two and play a game of cards. Yes, it was a hard life but an exciting one, much more exciting than staying in his village in Sylhet.

\* \* \*

Later that evening, when all the family was home, there was a conference. Ustad Miah's eldest son, Kalpana's dad, his daughter in law, their four older children including Kalpana, Ustad Miah's younger sons and their wives all crowded into the living room.

'Switch it off,' whispered Kalpana's mother to her youngest boy, Azad, who was fiddling with the volume of the TV. 'We have serious matters to discuss.'

Kalpana's father said, 'After what happened today, we must take drastic action to protect the girls in our family. These attacks are happening to many of our people and I don't want Kalpana suffering any more racial violence.'

The old grandfather spoke up. 'What is there to do except send her somewhere safer?'

Kalpana's eyes brimmed over with tears. 'I don't want to go far away to Bangladesh,' she cried, fearing the worst.

'Silly,' said her mother affectionately. 'Who's going to send you across the seas?'

'No, we've decided that Kalpana should go and stay with Afsarda in Sussex. She can go to school with his children and she will come home for the holidays,' said her father. His youngest brother, Afsar, owned a restaurant in Midhurst.

'No, no, I won't go away from home,' sobbed Kalpana. Her eyes were so red and swollen from crying that she could hardly see.

Her relatives started to speak all at once, saying that she must be sensible and that she would be with her uncle and aunt and cousins after all, but she couldn't hear any of their well-meant advice, only the sound of her own misery.

Ustad Miah beckoned to her. 'Come,' he said, holding her hand and drawing her near him. 'Listen to me, my precious child.' She sniffed and wiped her eyes. She had had a terrible experience but he wished he could prevent her from feeling crushed and defeated by it. He wanted to tell her that the world was much bigger than what she could see and experience at present. He wanted to tell her about the sights he had seen, about the people he had known, good and bad; about his fears and disappointments and his dreams and hopes. His life had been so rich and he had survived so many difficulties. His first wife, Gladdy, had died young. He'd met her selling raffle tickets in a pub. Then he'd gone back to Sylhet, married Kalpana's grandmother and brought her back to England. She had died a few years back. Now all his children and grandchildren were with him and he was happy.

'Do you know how old I was when I ran away to sea?' Of course, his grandchildren only knew the bare bones of his wonderful adventures when he was young. 'I was fourteen!' he whispered in her ear. 'But I lied to the foreman and said I was sixteen. I used to shave and try and make my beard come faster – and look how it grew,' he chuckled pulling at his long, snow-white beard which fanned out over his shirt front.

'You mustn't be afraid of what life brings and what has been ordained by Allah. I was never afraid,' he boasted, forgetting the lonely nights, the months at sea, the long hours of work in restaurants. 'All will be well, all will be well.'

Pratima Mitchell

# THE GREEKS

# Timon goes to school

'My name is Timon,' he says, 'I am eleven years old and I have been at school now for nearly five years.'

'What time do you get up?'

'I rise at dawn. Our rooster wakes me up early. My father says we borrowed rooster breeding from the Persians, but how my ancestors got themselves up before we had chickens, I don't know.

'I wash in cold water and my slave pours water all over me when I've finished. I dry myself and put my tunic on. In winter, I wear a cloak as well – and sandals also. In summer I go barefoot indoors and out.

'I eat a bread roll and wash it down with wine for breakfast. I say "wine" but it's really only water coloured pink with a little dash of wine. Even the grown-ups don't drink wine neat: they dilute it with more than the same amount of water.

'I walk to school which is a small corner of a building in an arcade of shops just off the agora. I give my personal slave, or pedagogue, as I call him, my writing tablets to carry on the way. He will protect me to and from classes and wait while I learn. I give the teacher the coins he charges for his lessons and we begin.'

'What do you learn?'

'History and Greek literature – and of course, how to read and write. We copy lines of Homer on to these waxed tablet boards with a pointed stick. The other end is blunt and flat. We use it to smooth out the wax if we make a mistake. We learn arithmetic with a bead frame, pebbles on the ground or even on our fingers. Some masters teach geometry and nearly all of them will tutor us in singing, speaking and playing the lyre, or flute.

'Later on we strip off in the nearby gymnasium and practise running, jumping, wrestling, boxing, throwing both the javelin and the discus and many other sports.

Then I wash, dress and go home. I can play toy soldiers with my brothers, while my sister (provided that she isn't helping my mother) has some rather nice dolls to dress and play with.

If there are no guests, we children sit up to the table on stools while father reclines on his couch. If there are guests, we eat separately before going to bed for the night.

From The Greeks by Roy Burrell

# The girl becomes a mother

Girl babies were often abandoned. 'If you bear a child,' a Greek soldier wrote to his wife, 'keep it if it is a boy. If it is a girl, cast it out.' In about 220 BC, a census (count) of the inhabitants of Miletus, a Greek city in Asia Minor, recorded 169 boys and only 46 girls.

At about the age of nine, a few Athenian girls were sent to 'act the bear' for a month in the Temple of Artemis, the goddess of hunting. They performed strange religious rituals which involved running around wildly. Some teenage girls joined the choirs which sang at religious festivals. In general, however, girls were 'given as little food as possible (and) were expected to keep their mouths shut and to attend to their wool'. In a Greek novel written to show husbands how to control their wives, the 15 year-old wife 'had lived under the strictest discipline, and had been taught to see, hear or ask as little as possible'. She did, however, know how to weave cloth and was a well-trained cook.

Fifteen was a common age for an Athenian girl to marry. Her husband would be nearer 30. The girl's father arranged her marriage, and paid the bridegroom a dowry. Most marriages took place in the winter month of Gamelion, the 'month of marriages'. The girl gave her toys to the Temple of Artemis, cut her hair, took a ritual bath in holy water and ate a last meal with her family. Then, at night, her husband and his friends arrived and took her away in a chariot (above). There was no wedding ceremony, although the groom's friends sang songs called hymns (after Hymen, the god of marriage).

Most Greek brides were terrified. One woman wrote: 'We are thrown out and sold away from our household gods and our parents. We go to the homes of men who may be strangers, foreigners, joyless or brutal. And once we are yoked to our husbands, we are forced to praise them and say all is well.

From I Was There: Ancient Greece by John D. Clare

# Enkales: my life as a slave

My name is Enkales (Enk-a-lees) and I am a slave. I'm a slave because my father was a slave and his father before him. It's said that my grandfather came from somewhere to the south of Egypt once long ago. He was on a voyage across the Mediterranean when his ship was attacked by pirates. They stole the cargo and sold all the people into slavery.'

'Is that how people become slaves in Greece?'

'Not the only the way, no. You could be kidnapped, captured as a prisoner of war or sold into bondage for debt. I don't think the last one is still used and I was told that the great Solon had done away with the custom of making a slave of any labourer who didn't work hard enough.

'It was Solon who freed all kinds of slaves: for instance, any Athenian who had to flee abroad to avoid slavery, any Athenian who had been sold in a foreign slave market or any Athenian who'd been made a slave here in Attica.

'My job is to look after the house, help with the shopping, chopping wood and getting it in, buying charcoal for the cooking fire and fetching all the household water from the public fountain. I also do all the odd jobs that crop up around the house as well as walking the young master to and from school when his regular slave can't do it.

'It's hard work most of the time but I suppose I'm better off than some slaves. I'm talking about those who work in the mines. I overheard a house guest the other day. He had rented part of the silver mines at Laurium. He and scores of other mine men bought up to a dozen or so slaves each and set them to work. They had absolutely wretched conditions to toil in.

'Most of the time they worked until they dropped in hot, wet darkness, breaking their backs to fill leather bags with lumps of rock which they had smashed with pickaxes and crowbars. Their owners' attitude seemed to be "Slaves are cheap, so keep them at it until they fall exhausted". In fact, slaves aren't all that cheap –'

We interrupt to try and find out how dear they were in terms we can understand. It seems that it would have taken the complete earnings of a modern average workman for six or seven weeks to buy a male slave.

'Anyway,' says Enkales, 'there are even now as many as twenty or thirty thousand poor devils slaving away in those silver mines.'

'Couldn't they complain?'

'You obviously don't know much about the set up in Athens. No slave is allowed to vote or speak in the Assembly and as for having a revolt – well! We'd never get enough of them to do the same thing at the same time. Why, they come from so many different parts of the world, you can't even find a language they all understand. Some of them don't speak a word of Greek – especially the mineworkers.'

'Do slaves work on the land?'

'Yes, but not as many as Sparta, or some of the other cities, use to farm with. Even so, it's been worked out that almost half of all the people who live in Athens are slaves. Many of us are house slaves and others work in quarries, docks or workshops, making things.

'I suppose the owners of these businesses have to be careful not to employ too many slaves or no free man would ever find work. As it is, most households have about three slaves on average.

'A slave can, if he's lucky, buy himself out. All he needs is to lay his hands on a lot of money. I've already said that house slaves are better off than those who work in quarries or mines but all of us suffer in a way I've not told you about yet.'

'What's that?'

'Well, if ever any one of us is called upon to give evidence in a court case – are you sure you don't know about this?'

We shake our heads.

'The rule is, that however a slave is connected with a trial, even if he's only an innocent bystander, he must be tortured first before his evidence is taken, because they believe he will tell lies otherwise!

'You can see that it's not such a golden age for us!'

From The Greeks by Roy Burrell

# Sea battle

When the Persians invade Athens, Aster and her family flee to the island of Salamis. The Persians then try to invade Salamis and find that they have been lured into a trap.

That night I woke, and rose, and went out into the night to listen. I thought I heard the splashing of oars, the creaking of timber, coming to me faintly over the still water. I grinned to myself, thinking of the Persians tiring themselves out at the oar, waiting for an enemy to come escaping past them, who would not come, but were sleeping quietly, gathering strength for the morning! Oh, just let the morning come!

And when it came, instead of the golden calm of still waters, there were the warships of the Persians, filling the strait, hundreds upon hundreds of them, and crowding onwards as far as the eye could see, terrible and splendid, blazing with armed men on the decks. Their raked ranks of oars beat like wings, and churned the sea to frothy white; they cawed to each other with the hoarse voices of brazen trumpets.

Cries of terror and dismay rang from the camp of the people, while I laughed with joy and gladness! It had worked; they had come to their doom; and I was the only one that knew it was a triumph and not a disaster.

Then, even as people began to run, as if to warn unsuspecting generals that the enemy were upon them, we heard another sound – the deep quiet sound of men singing. Hidden behind the promontory our ships were on the move; and hundreds of Greek voices were singing the solemn Paeon to our gods. Within minutes the line of our ships came into view, moving across the strait to close it to the Persians, and swinging round to meet them head on.

Upon so terrible a sight as that battle, I could not look long; my heart had not the strength for it. I watched the first line of the Persians come up to our ships; I heard cries, and trumpets, and the loud rending of splintered hulls. I saw that the Persians were pressing forwards too fast, just where the channel narrowed like a funnel, and they were fouling each other's oars, and coming to a helpless standstill just within reach of harm. And I laughed, and was as proud of Themistokles as though he had been brother or father of mine. But I could not look long.

At noon I climbed the height, and looked down at the whole crooked channel choked with ships. I could not discern what was happening, or, from so far off, clearly tell our ships from theirs, but I could see from far off more ships coming up to help them. And I thought we could not possibly win against so many.

Towards evening, when they began to flee away, past us, all broken and disabled, and with our triremes in full pursuit, I looked again. And the water was all curdled and thick with wreckage, and with floating men. A foul detritus of smashed timber and dead men had washed up on the beaches. The dead wore strange armour, with overlapping scales like lizards, and their wounds were washed white by the sea. I crept away, and hid myself in our tent, and took no part in the joy and dancing, and celebrating among the people.

From *Crossing to Salamis* by Jill Paton Walsh

# The wooden horse

One morning the Trojans awoke to see a cloud of smoke hanging over the Greek camp. To their surprise they discovered that the Greeks had gone leaving their camp in ashes. The only thing that remained was a huge wooden statue of a horse.

The Trojans were mystified. What could it mean? Some wanted to drag the statue up but others were highly suspicious and demanded that it be burnt. King Priam was loathe to desecrate the statue risking the wrath of the goddess. He ordered it to be hauled across the plain on rollers. When they reached the town they found that the statue was far too large to get through the gates and part of the walls had to be dismantled. The statue stuck four times but finally they got it through and rebuilt the wall behind them. Sweating in the heat of the day they laboriously began to haul the great statue up the steep street but they found the route blocked by Priam's strange but beautiful daughter Cassandra and the Prophet Laocoön.

'It's full of men!' screamed Cassandra. But Priam's supporters shouted her down.

'She's mad! Everybody knows it!'

Priam ordered the men to continue.

'You fools! Never trust a Greek bringing gifts!' shouted Laocoön and hurled his spear at the horse.

The weapon stuck quivering in the wood and there was a distinct clatter of metal inside the statue.

'Burn it,' screamed some of the mob. 'Hurl it over the walls.'

Amidst all the din and commotion a prisoner was being dragged up the street. It was Odysseus' cousin, Sinon. When the Greek saw Priam he threw himself at the old king's feet and begged his protection. He told the king how he had been hounded by Odysseus.

'Once we were close friends,' he sobbed, 'but since Ajax's death Odysseus has changed. He is now embittered and suspicious of all those around him. He accused me of being a coward and a cheat. He had me arrested and would have killed me if I hadn't escaped last night when they were launching the ships.'

Priam interrupted him.

'Tell us about the horse.'

Sinon explained that the Greeks had fallen foul of Athena.

'In fact that was the reason they gave up the siege. The horse was built to try to placate the angry goddess.'

'But why is it so big?' Priam asked.

'Oh,' Sinon laughed, 'that was so that you wouldn't be able to bring it into the city.'

Priam was convinced and ordered the horse to be dragged on up to the sanctuary of Athena where he dedicated it to the goddess. Girls went down into the plain to gather flowers along the river banks and made garlands to decorate the statue.

That evening Helen came to look at the horse. She walked round the huge statue occasionally tapping it and calling out the names of the various heroes. Then she turned and smiled at her husband, Deiphobus.

'Of course they aren't inside it,' she scoffed.

That night the Trojans held a great feast to celebrate their victory. Around midnight Odysseus' cousin, Sinon, slipped out and lit a beacon. The signal was seen on the heights of the island of Tenedos and passed on to Agamemnon who was waiting with the fleet. By the light of the moon the Greeks clambered aboard their ships and strained at their oars until the black hulls were skimming across the glittering water.

The Trojans were still in a drunken slumber after their riotous night of celebrations. They did not see a door open in the belly of the horse nor did they see the shadowy figures climbing down with their armour glinting in the first light of dawn.

From The Legend of Odysseus by Peter Connolly

# Who was Odysseus?

Was there a real king of Ithaca called Odysseus? We can never know, but we may guess that there was because the hero of Homer's *Odyssey* seems such a real person. He is certainly more human than other ancient heroes.

At first sight he did not look much like a hero, because he was not very tall. When he stood up to make a speech he was not such a grand figure of a man as Agamemnon or Menelaus. But when he began to speak he was much more impressive. All Greek princes were taught the art of public speaking as part of their education and Odysseus was the best speaker among the heroes at Troy.

Though not tall, he was broad and strong. Marching among his men, someone said, he looked like a ram among sheep. His hair was reddish (a common colour among the Greeks) but his beard was dark.

He was not such a mighty warrior as Achilles, but he was a brave fighter. In his last great battle, against the men who had taken over his palace in Ithaca, he killed them with arrows from a bow no one else was strong enough to draw. Odysseus' greatest qualities were his cunning and intelligence. He was the cleverest of the Greeks, the man they always called on to get them out of a difficult spot. It had to be Odysseus who thought of the Wooden Horse, or of escaping from Polyphemus' cave by clinging to the belly of a sheep. Heroes were not usually this crafty. They almost despised cleverness. If Achilles had been still alive he would probably have said that the Wooden Horse was a sneaky trick.

Odysseus was less proud, less high and mighty, than other heroes. His kingdom was a small faraway island and his ancestors were not very distinguished, but they were remarkable. This was an important matter to the Greeks. Who you were depended on who your ancestors were. It is true that Odysseus counted Zeus (king of the gods) as one of his ancestors. But that was common, almost necessary. Any Greek hero worth his salt was descended from Zeus and usually from several other gods and goddesses as well.

From The World of Odysseus by Neil Grant

# A whirlpool and a monster

After the fall of Troy, Odysseus sets sail for his island kingdom of Ithaca. On the journey he confronts many dangers, including the Sirens whose sweet songs lure sailors to their deaths, the whirlpool Charybdis and the six-headed monster, Scylla.

'When we reached the ship I told my men what lay ahead and warned them in particular of the Sirens whom we would encounter first. They have the most beautiful voices and lure sailors ashore with their songs. Their island is littered with the dead bodies of these unfortunate men. I had been told how I could hear their songs and still survive.

'As we approached the island the wind dropped. The crew lowered the sail and ran out the oars. While they rowed I went round plugging their ears with wax. Then they bound me to the mast and returned to their oars.

Soon I heard sweet voices calling to me across the water. They called my name. Their alluring sound was more than I could bear. I signalled to my men to release me but they only bound me tighter and strained at the oars until those seductive voices faded in the distance.

'My men had barely released me when we saw a cloud of black smoke. We were approaching the mountain of the dreaded Scylla whose peak is always shrouded in dark smoke. The Scylla is a twelve footed monster with six long necks each ending in a fearsome head with three rows of teeth. It lives in a cave half way up the mountain. I had been told that there was no defence against the Scylla as no arrow could reach its cave.

Nevertheless, I armed myself and stood at the front of the ship. I ordered the helmsman to hug the mountain. I knew this was leaving us wide open to the Scylla but anything was better than being dragged down by the Charybdis.

'The Charybdis lies opposite the Scylla. It is a whirlpool which sucks down the dark waters and then throws them up again. It is situated at the foot of a cliff crowned by a huge fig tree.

'We sailed up the straight, hugging the sheer face of the mountain and gazing in horror at the whirlpool as it sucked down the water and spurted it up again drenching the cliffs with spray. As we rowed desperately along its perimeter we could see right down into its vortex to the bed of the sea itself. My gaze was transfixed in terror. Suddenly I heard someone screaming my name and I looked up to see six of my men dangling in the air above me. For a moment I heard their screams and then there was silence. The Scylla had taken its toll.

'The horror was over. We were now approaching the island of Thrinacie. The blind prophet had warned me to avoid it but my men were verging on mutiny after their last experience so I agreed to let them camp overnight on the beach as long as each man swore an oath not to touch the Sun-god's cattle.

'That night a storm broke and I knew that we were likely to be stuck on the island several days. We had plenty of food with us and we would not go hungry. But the gales lasted for a month. Our food ran out and finally the pangs of hunger overcame my men's scruples. They ate some of the Sun-god's cattle.

'When the winds dropped we put to sea. Clouds gathered and we were hit by a violent storm. The rigging was ripped apart and the mast fell on the helmsman. Lightning struck the ship and finally a great wave ripped the sides apart. We were plunged into the water and that was the last I saw of my companions.

'I lashed the mast and keel together and climbed onto them. The westerly gale soon blew itself out but a southerly gale took over and to my horror began to drive me back towards the Charybdis. I felt the drag of the current. As I was whirled beneath the cliff I leaped up and grabbed the overhanging branches of the fig tree. There I hung watching my make-shift raft whirl round faster and faster until it disappeared. It seemed ages before it was thrown up again. I dropped into the water, struggled on to the timbers and rowed with my hands. Nine days later I was washed up on the island of Ogygia where the nymph Calypso lives.

'I owe my life to Calypso but she refused to let me leave. For eight years I languished there. Finally the gods ordered her to release me. I built a boat in which I sailed across the open sea for seventeen days before being shipwrecked and washed ashore here.'

The audience had listened spellbound. They escorted Odysseus to the ship that the king had prepared for him and loaded him with presents.

From The Legend of Odysseus by Peter Connolly

# The story of Daedalus and Icarus

A spoilt boy needs a strong father. That is undoubtedly true. But then a boy with a strong father would naturally not be spoilt. Thus mused Daedalus, the King's architect, as he wandered along the summer sea-shore, listening to the gulls' squawking and quarrelling, and watching their endless swooping and wheeling and diving. He kicked with his sandal at a pebble and sent it skittering through the dry sand, amused at his own thoughts. Tonight he would tell them to King Minos, making it into a riddle: 'What is it that a spoilt boy needs but can never have?' It should amuse the King and perhaps he would give Daedalus more gold for the work he had done recently. The architect smiled again at the thought but then looked upwards sharply as a cry came from above.

'Father!' the word fell on the wind from the cliff-top. High above him Daedalus could see his son Icarus, standing on the very edge of the cliff where the rocks were crumbling, his arms spread as if he were about to dive on to the rocks below.

'No!' cried Daedalus, his heart in his mouth. 'No, Icarus! Go back!'

With a mocking laugh the boy dropped his arms and stepped back from the edge of the cliff. It had been just another of his stupid tricks.

As Daedalus walked on along the beach he worried about his son, knowing that if he had been a strong father Icarus would have been beaten many times for trying to scare him and worry him, for no reason other than devilment. But then – he shrugged and his lips twisted wryly as he remembered the saying 'Strong men don't have spoilt sons'.

Another shout made him turn to see two of King Minos' men running down the beach towards him.

'Daedalus!' they shouted. 'King Minos needs you immediately.'

The architect was surprised but rather pleased. Perhaps Minos was going to offer him the building job for which he had hoped. He turned and walked quickly back to the palace, laughing and chattering with the soldiers. He waited in the cool marble hall while a message was taken in to Minos to say that he had arrived.

Daedalus looked round the familiar hall which he himself had designed and built as an addition to the Palace several years ago. He admired the painted frescoes on the walls showing Cretan youths and maidens running, hurling spears and leaping over slab-bodied bulls. He thought about having similar frescoes painted on the walls of the Labyrinth – that underground maze of black tunnels he had built for Minos. But no, it was so dark in the maze that no-one would see them – and in any case no-one lived long enough to appreciate paintings there. The Minotaur was swift and merciless in his killing.

The architect's thoughts were suddenly interrupted by a bellow of rage from within. He took quick steps into the King's room, where he found Minos, legs astride and arms raised above his head, absolutely furious. The two soldiers were cowering before him, one holding the left side of his face which showed the fiery red imprint of the King's fingers. Minos turned and bore down on Daedalus like an enraged bull. Daedalus fell to his knees, afraid for his life, wondering what had happened make the King so angry. He covered his face with his hands as he saw Minos reach towards the jewelled dagger at his belt.

'Stupid, blundering, incompetent idiot!' yelled the King. Daedalus flinched. He said nothing for there was nothing to say.

'Snivelling, lame-brained fool,' said the King. 'Get ready to die.'

'But Lord, what have I done?' whimpered Daedalus.

The King drew back his sandalled foot and lashed out wickedly, but Daedalus threw himself backwards out of range across the floor.

'Daedalus,' said the King in a quiet voice that was even more menacing than his bellow.

'Yes, my Lord King?'

'Do you remember the Labyrinth?'

'My Lord?'

How could he forget? It had been the biggest triumph of his life, building the maze so cleverly that nobody who set foot in it could ever again find his way out.

'No-one can ever escape from it, so you said,' went on Minos.

'That's right, my Lord, I'd stake my life on it.'

'Then prepare to die. For last night, I'm told, your famous Labyrinth's secret was broken, my sacred Minotaur killed, and my most precious prisoner allowed to escape.'

'But nobody could escape without help, my lord.'

The King roared again. 'He *had* help, fool! Of course he had help. But in the end he escaped, and you had said he couldn't. And for that you will surely die.' His hand again went towards the dagger, but then stopped.

'Take him away,' he snarled at the soldiers. 'Shut him in the tower while I make up my mind how to kill him slowly. One day and one night, Daedalus and then ...' he drew his finger across his fat throat with a hiss and then turned away.

Alone in the damp cell in the tower, Daedalus waited. Within the hour the door opened and his son Icarus was flung in beside him, crying, bewildered, all the tricks knocked out of him, but full of petulant questions.

Daedalus, for the first time in his life, spoke sharply, telling him to save his tears for when he had to die. The boy went off to sulk in the corner while Daedalus paced the cell, thinking.

An hour went by and Icarus spoke. 'Father,' he said in his spoilt, whining voice, 'you've got to get us out of here.'

Daedalus ignored him, but then sighed, shrugged his shoulders and went over to the door to whisper through the keyhole.

'Pssst!' he hissed. Outside the guard shuffled his feet.

'Pssst! Guard!'

'What do you want, Daedalus?' The guard was one of the two who had brought him from the Palace, and an old friend.

'Do you like gold?'

'Do donkeys like strawberries?'

'Here then. I shall have no use for it soon.' There was a tinkle as Daedalus pushed a coin through a crack between the timbers of the door.

'Would you like some more?'

'Yes, oh yes, Master Daedalus.' The soldier sounded eager.

'Then open the door and I will show you gold, more gold than you have ever imagined.'

The bolt creaked and the door opened. As the guard thrust his grizzled head into the cell, Daedalus with a sigh brought down a heavy stool on it. The guard collapsed in a heap and Daedalus and Icarus slipped down the stone steps and ran low towards the sea-cliffs as fast as their legs would carry them.

'Poor friend,' thought Daedalus as they ran, thinking of the soldier. 'Well, he didn't see gold but at least he saw golden stars!' He caught hold of his son's hand to help him over the rough tussocks of grass. Then he turned off the path, pushed aside the low branches of a flowering bush and scrambled through the entrance of a cave, dragging Icarus behind him. Inside it felt damp and there was little light, but at least they were safe for the time being, safe while Daedalus thought of a way to escape from the island.

Icarus was bad-tempered, full of nagging questions. 'I don't like this cave, father. Why can't we go back to our own home? Why is the King angry with us?'

'Quiet, Icarus, while I think.'

The boy went sulkily towards the entrance of the cave where it was lighter and passed the time playing with some birds' feathers which he found on the floor. He lifted them above his head and let them drift down to the floor again. Daedalus watched, an idea slowly forming in his mind. If he could find enough feathers, and find something to hold them together, then he was sure he could make wings. With wings he and Icarus could leave the island safely and fly over the sea, out of the reach of King Minos.

'We'll fly!' he said loudly and stood up suddenly. 'Now Icarus, for once listen carefully and do as you are told, for our lives depend on it. Run down to the beach and gather as many large gulls' feathers as you can find. Bring them back here. Don't argue, go at once.'

'But father,' began the boy, then let out a sudden howl. For the first time in his life he felt the smack of his father's hand on the back of his head. The blow was painful but it served its purpose. Sobbing with rage and wounded pride Icarus scuttled off to do as he was told, while Daedalus walked to a nearby wood looking up into the trees.

Much later, as the sun was setting, Icarus and Daedalus returned to the cave. To give him credit, the boy had done well and had managed to gather a large pile of white and grey feathers. Daedalus too had found what he had looked for.

'See,' he said holding out his arms which were covered with red blotches.

'What happened, father? Your arms look as if they had been stung by bees.'

'And quite right too. You see I need something to keep the feathers together when I make the wings, and I thought of wax. There's always wax in a bees' nest, but the bees don't usually like it when you take it off them.' Daedalus smiled grimly.

It was a long night. Icarus slept fitfully on the damp sand, but Daedalus sat and worked at the mouth of the cave where the moonlight filtered through the flowery bush.

And when the sun's first rays came over the eastern horizon, the wings were ready. Icarus was very excited and fussed around while his father tore his tunic into lengths to fasten the wings to their shoulders. As soon as they were ready, the two moved out of the cave, looked around cautiously to make sure that they were not being followed and then went up to the highest point on the cliff.

Down below the surf foamed over the black rocks. Grey gulls launched themselves from tiny ledges and lay on the wind effortlessly. The cliff-top breeze ruffled the feathers on Daedalus's wings and once again Icarus was whining.

'Father, these wings are uncomfortable.'

'Then the sooner we get them off the better. Now listen. When we are flying flap the wings strongly but slowly. That way you will be able to keep going for a long time. Fly low with me over the sea, so that if anything goes wrong we are not so high that a fall will hurt us. Are you ready?'

'Yes, father, but...' The rest of the words were lost in a shrill scream as Daedalus lifted his hand, placed it in the small of his son's back and pushed him off the cliff's edge. The boy fell, wings flapping wildly, until at last, clumsily but then with more skill, he was flying! Daedalus held his breath, closed his eyes and then he too jumped to join Icarus in the air.

For a while the two spent time getting used to the wings and the strange wonderful new experience, but then Daedalus pointed out to sea and they headed away from the rising sun and away to freedom.

For a time all went very well. The wings were big and strong, and the two flew over the wave crests, feeling the spray cold on their trailing toes, laughing at the ease with which they were travelling. Daedalus felt hope rising inside him, and even began to think about their future when they finally reached the other side of the sea. Perhaps Sicily would be the best place for them to seek refuge, safe enough and far enough away from Minos to be out of reach and out of danger.

A delighted shout roused him from these thoughts and he looked up to see that his son had disobeyed his orders and was flying far above him, shouting to his father to admire his cleverness. As he watched Icarus spiralled again upwards.

'Come down!' called Daedalus, but his words, and the boy's reply were lost in the rush of the wind and the spray.

'Come down, you stupid boy!' called Daedalus, sobbing with dismay and anger. A new thought suddenly struck him. Apart from the danger of the boy falling to his death from such a great height, there was also another danger. Up there the sun would be hotter and would burn down on the wax – everyone knows wax melts in the heat – and the wing feathers were only held together with wax ...

'Come down, Icarus!' called Daedalus again. He started to go up himself after his son, but even as he rose he knew it was too late. There was a long frightened scream from above, a large struggling shape flashed past him, then a very faint splash from below. The cry hung on the wind for a second then it too was lost.

The sky was empty except for Daedalus, hovering and looking down. But the surface of the sea showed no trace of the few ripples that had been made when Icarus plunged downwards to his death.

Daedalus took a huge breath, then flew onwards towards Sicily. Inside his body he wept for the death of his son. The boy had always been spoilt, and if only he had been a stronger father then perhaps he would have been alive still. A solitary tear welled up in his eye and fell to the waves below. A gull squawked. And Daedalus flew on.

*From Myths and Legends Book 1: Classical and northern stories by David Oakden*

# Theseus and the Minotaur

Theseus had reached the age of seventeen before he learned that his father was Aegeus, king of Athens. As soon as he discovered this he set off for Athens as fast as he could. He was a brave young man, skilled in the art of weapons. On the way to find his father Theseus met, and killed, many strange monsters. By the time he reached Athens his reputation for bravery had gone before him.

Aegeus was overjoyed to see his son and Theseus was pleased to have found his father, but he soon realized that something bad was happening in Athens. People's faces were drawn and pale. They spoke in strange whispers and there was no laughing. Into the harbour sailed a ship with black sails.

Every seven years seven young girls and seven young men were chosen by lottery. They sailed off in the ship with black sails. This was Athens' tribute to King Minos of Crete. No one in Athens ever knew what really happened to the young men and women. They knew only that it was to do with the Minotaur.

Years before King Minos had angered Poseidon, god of the sea. As punishment Poseidon sent the Minotaur to Crete. This savage creature had the body of a man and the head of a bull, and ate human flesh. The Minotaur went wild and killed many people. It almost destroyed the whole of Crete. King Minos had a labyrinth built, deep underground. A network of tunnels so complicated that no one who wandered in could ever get out. The Minotaur was put at the centre of the Labyrinth and left there alone. Alone that is until the young people of Athens arrived, and they did not last long.

Theseus was horrified when he learned why the young people were boarding the ship. He decided he would go to Crete himself and destroy the Minotaur. He went onto the ship instead of one of the young men and in place of two of the young women he put soldiers, dressed up to look like girls. Aegeus begged Theseus not to go but when he saw his son was determined he gave him a white sail.

'When you return,' he said, 'Raise this white sail so that I will know you have been successful.'

When the ship with black sails arrived at Crete King Minos was waiting. He watched the young people climb from the ship and ordered that they be locked in a prison until it was time to send them into the Labyrinth. Also watching at the quay side was a young girl called Ariadne. She was the daughter of King Minos. She looked at Theseus as he passed. There was something in his eyes that made her realise this was no ordinary Athenian.

That night she went to the prison to see Theseus. When he realized that she may help him he explained how he had come to kill the Minotaur.

'I will help you,' said Ariadne. 'But you must take me back to Athens with you when you have killed the monster.'

Theseus agreed and later in the night Ariadne returned with a key to set him free.

'I have brought you a sword,' she whispered. 'And a ball of wool. Play out the wool as you go into the Labyrinth and you will be able to follow it back out. Without it you would never escape from the tunnels. No one has ever come out alive.'

She led Theseus to the entrance of the Labyrinth. With the sword in one hand and the ball of wool in the other Theseus stepped into the darkness. Inside the tunnel the walls glowed with a strange green light. The air smelt of death and decay and everything was damp. He walked through tunnel after tunnel, playing out the wool as he walked along. Every passage-way looked the same and the cold seemed to seep into his bones. After a while the ball of wool ran out and Theseus stopped.

'Where are you?' he whispered in the silence. And then louder. 'Where are you?'

Something stirred.

There was a scraping noise behind Theseus and when he turned he saw a bulky figure standing in one of the archways. It stepped forward.

The Minotaur was horrible. More horrible than anyone could have imagine. It was tall and naked. Up to the neck it was human but its head was that of a bull. Two large horns curved out of its head and its teeth were like those of a lion. Its face and skin were matted with a mixture of dirt and dried blood and its breath was like the breath of dead men.

The Minotaur rushed forward swinging a large, twisted iron club. Theseus knocked the club aside with his sword. The Minotaur roared with surprise. No one had ever fought back before. Its orange eyes flashed and saliva dripped from its mouth as it rushed forward once again. As the Minotaur lowered its head to spike Theseus with its filthy horns the young Athenian dodged to one side and with a single blow severed the beast's head.

Silence settled like dust in the coldness of the labyrinth.

Tired and drenched in the Minotaur's blood, Theseus followed the woollen thread until at last he found himself out in the open air. Day was dawning. Ariadne had been busy during the night. She had freed all the Athenians. The soldiers who had dressed as girls had taken them all to the ship and there they were waiting for Theseus. As the last star left the morning sky they rowed out of the harbour and away from the Island of Crete. When Minos discovered that the Minotaur was dead he was so grateful he forgave Theseus for taking away his daughter.

And so the story ends, or very nearly. Some say that Ariadne fell ill and died. Others that Theseus broke his promise and abandoned her on the island of Naxos. No one really knows. One thing is certain, Theseus forgot to change the black sail for the white one. When Aegeus saw the black sail coming he thought his son had been killed and in despair threw himself into the sea. Ever afterwards the sea has been called the Aegean.

Theseus became king of Athens and did many great things. He was the first king of Athens to mint money. Should you ever find one of Theseus's coins you will recognize it immediately. On it is stamped the head of a bull!

Robin Mellor

# Apples of the gods

Hercules (Heracles) was the son of Zeus and the mortal Alcmene. Hera, the wife of Zeus, sent two snakes to kill Hercules when he was still a baby, but he strangled both of them. Hercules married the Theban king's daughter, Megara, but was driven mad by Hera, so that he killed his wife, his own children and two nephews. As punishment he was required to serve his cousin Eurystheus, King of Argos, for twelve years. The king gave Hercules twelve seemingly impossible tasks to carry out – the Labours of Hercules. At the end of this time he was to become immortal. One of the tasks that Hercules was commanded to perform was to bring back the Golden Apples of the Hesperides from Mount Atlas.

So Hercules journeyed to the remote region where the immense tower of Mount Atlas thrust itself up to brush against the sky. There, sure-footed and tireless, he clambered up its rugged slopes until, within bowshot of the summit, he found a plateau that bore upon it a wonderful garden. And in the midst of the garden's rich grasses and delicate flowers he saw a gigantic wall of hewn blocks of stone each as large as a house.

Hercules sprang easily to the top of the wall – and there before him was the spreading foliage of the sacred tree. Glistening among the leaves he saw the radiant gold of the apples which he had come for. And, coiled round the trunk of the tree, he saw the scaly form of the dragon, its head turning this way and that, its tongue flicking restlessly past rows of fangs like javelin points.

He shook his head glumly. How easy it might have been to dispatch the dragon with an arrow, then leap down and gather the golden apples. The work of moments – yet the rage of Hera would pursue him afterwards, for years.

But was there anyone else foolish enough to risk that same rage?

As he pondered, he heard from above his head – from the crest of the mountain – a mighty, gusty groan, deep and hollow and full of pain. Hercules knew at once who had made the sound. It would be the master of this mountain, he who had given it its name, the earth-shaking giant among giants, the Titan called Atlas.

Instantly Hercules dropped down from the wall and sprang up the almost sheer ascent towards the mountain peak.

He had encountered Titans before, and knew much about their towering size and strength, and about the world-rending war, long ago, which they had fought with the Olympian gods for mastery of the earth. So he expected Atlas to loom almost like a mountain himself, as hugely as Hercules would loom over a year-old child.

He had not expected to find, on that summit, that Atlas's vast frame would be

stooped almost double – beneath a burden so monstrous that Hercules could not imagine why it had not crushed even the Titan as a man's boot would flatten an insect.

The burden was nothing less than the sky itself – the mighty vault of Heaven, arching above the earth like a colossal crystalline sphere studded with stars. It was at the tallest mountain peaks where the supports of Heaven had been placed by the Most Ancient Beings who had created the earth and sea and sky. But after that terrible war when the gods of Olympus had defeated the Titans, Zeus had punished the most powerful Titan warrior, Atlas, by ordering that Atlas must stand for all time on the pinnacle of his own mountain and be himself the pillar of the Heavens.

And it was that unimaginable weight that brought forth, now and then, from the Titan's chest the tormented groan that Hercules had heard.

Hercules drew closer, staring up at the huge craggy face twisted with its look of eternal effort. 'Lord Atlas, I am Hercules, come to seek your help with a task I must do as punishment.'

The great head turned slowly. 'Aid?' the Titan replied. 'I have a punishment of my own, little human, as you see. I can aid no other's.'

'But you can,' said Hercules. 'I am required to gather the golden apples from the tree of Hera, and Zeus himself has shown me how it might be done. But I cannot do it alone.'

The huge eyes of Atlas blinked in slow thoughtfulness. 'The apples ... yes, I remember. I cherished them once, before this burden was put upon me. They are nothing to me now – take them if you will. But I cannot aid you.'

'Could you not,' Hercules persisted, 'set down your burden for less than an hour?'

The Titan sighed, like the tide rushing within a vast sea-cave. 'Would that I could do so, even for only the space of a breath.' And then Hercules saw a slow smile begin to spread across the great face – a smile of such obvious and open craftiness that it might almost have been comic. 'Yet,' Atlas went on, 'if there were someone strong enough to support the Heavens in my place, only for a few moments ... Then you might have my aid.'

Hercules' eyes widened. Never had even his superhuman strength been faced with anything like the awesomeness of that burden. He was by no means sure he could manage it. And he was wholly sure that behind the Titan's smile lay the clear intention never to take up the burden again, if once he could give it up.

Still, Hercules had no choice, and he was not one to back away from any challenge. 'Very well, lord Atlas, I will take up your burden – while you gather the apples.'

'Are you strong enough, little human?' Atlas frowned. 'The Heavens must not fall, or the gods' wrath will know no limits.'

Hercules set his jaw. 'Let me take the weight, and we will see if my back can bear it.'

So he stood beside the Titan, planted his feet and gritted his teeth. And slowly Atlas bent lower, and carefully the inconceivable weight of the Heavens was lowered until at last the whole of it rested upon the back and shoulders of Hercules.

He might have screamed, had he been able to spare the breath. It was a crushing pressure beyond all nightmares. Sweat gushed from Hercules like waterfalls; his legs began to tremble, every vein swelled to bursting, every joint of his body cracked with the strain, every thew and tendon shrieked their agony at the stresses that went to the very limits, and beyond, of even their awesome power.

Yet he was Hercules, who had never admitted defeat. With every grim ounce of determination he forced his quivering limbs into stillness, forced back the waves of crippling pain – and stood, fixed and solid as if hewn from granite, and held the vault of Heaven secure.

'Stronger you are than I would have dreamed,' marvelled the Titan, grinning. 'Now I will do my part. But what of the sleepless dragon who guards the street?'

'My ... bow,' Hercules gasped through clenched teeth. 'Poisoned arrows ... nothing can survive them.'

So Atlas laughed with glee, gathered up the weapons and trudged off down the mountain. Within moments Hercules heard the thrum of his bowstring and the strangled hissing death-cry of the dragon. And soon after, the giant form of the Titan loomed again before Hercules' pain-blurred eyes.

'It is done,' Atlas boomed happily, holding up a glowing handful of the golden apples.

'My thanks,' Hercules grated. 'Now I ... shall go my way.'

'Not just yet,' rumbled the grinning Titan. 'You cannot imagine the joy I feel at my freedom, able again to stand straight and walk unburdened in the sun and wind.'

'I can imagine ... very well,' Hercules grunted.

'I have it in my mind,' Atlas went on, ignoring him, 'to take these apples with me and wander the earth awhile, to see all the things that have come to pass since I first was imprisoned on this mountain. It may be,' and his grin widened, 'that one day I shall grow weary of wandering, and come back to relieve you of your burden. So wait here for me, little one, and watch for my return.'

And he laughed a huge booming laugh in delight at his own cleverness.

Hercules might also have laughed at the Titan's belief that he had tricked Hercules. But instead he let his face sag, as one who has been defeated and must accept his fate.

'Go, then ... I will bear the burden ... as I must. But first I crave ... your aid ... in one more thing.'

Atlas smiled expansively. 'In my joy, little human, I feel there is little I could deny you.'

'This vast weight ... sits awkwardly,' Hercules gasped, 'for I am not as strong ... as you. I could bear it more easily ... if I could make a pad ... of my lionskin ... for my head and neck.'

Atlas scratched his vast beard in slow thought. 'Yes, I can see how that would help.'

'Then take ... the weight of Heaven,' Hercules went on, 'while I make myself ready.'

'Certainly,' said Atlas foolishly. 'Anything to ease the burden for the one to whom I owe my freedom.'

And he bowed his huge empty head and bent his back and lifted up the Heavens again from the shoulders of Hercules. As the weight left him,

Hercules sank to his knees, his head swimming. But almost at once strength and energy flowed back into his freed muscles. And he stood up and began calmly gathering up the golden apples.

'Hold, now,' rumbled Atlas, watching with puzzlement. 'What of this pad for your neck?'

Hercules smiled. 'O Atlas, you were right when you spoke of the joy of standing free and unburdened. I too am of no mind to give up that pleasure.'

The giant face twisted with anger. 'You have tricked me! You never intended to take up the burden again!'

'No more than you did,' laughed Hercules, 'when you went to pluck the golden apples. And for that my gratitude – for now they are mine, yet it was not I who committed the theft.'

And as the Titan roared with frustrated fury, Hercules turned and began his descent from the mountain-top.

From The Exploits of Hercules by Douglas Hill

# King Midas and his gold

Once upon a time there was a king called Midas. He was very rich. He lived in a marble palace decorated with gold. He had a golden throne to sit on and a golden crown to wear on his head.

He had chests full of treasures – golden necklaces, golden bracelets, and golden rings. Inside his palace he had trees made by clever craftsmen, with gold and silver leaves. The fruit that hung from the branches was made of precious jewels. Emerald and ruby, amethyst and topaz and lapis lazuli.

One day, the men who worked in Midas's garden found an old, shabby man asleep among the rose bushes. They tied his hands and feet with garlands of roses, and carried him as their prisoner to King Midas.

'Who are you? And what are you doing in my garden?' Midas asked the man.

'Great King, the god of wine, Dionysus, has many followers. I am one of them. I am old Silenus. If you will set me free so that I can join him again, I will tell you the most wonderful stories you have ever heard.'

Midas kept Silenus in his palace for five days and nights, and he listened to his stories.

'I will tell you,' said Silenus, 'how there is a great land, far away beyond the sea. It is full of splendid cities, and the people who live there are happy and tall and they live nearly for ever. Or shall I tell you about the terrible whirlpool which no human has ever been able to cross?

'Nearby are two streams, and on the banks of the streams grow two different kinds of tree. The man who eats the fruit of the first kind becomes miserable and he cries and groans until he dies. The man who eats the fruit of the second kind of tree grows younger every day. Even old men can become babies again.'

After hearing these stories, Midas let Silenus go.

The god Dionysus sent a message to Midas. 'I will reward you for looking after my old friend. Tell me what your dearest wish is and I will grant it.'

Midas said at once, 'I should like best that everything I touch should turn into gold.'

'Think carefully what you are asking for,' Dionysus said.

But Midas would not stop to think. He wanted to be the richest man in the world.

Dionysus said, 'Then I will grant your wish. From now on, you have the Golden Touch.'

Midas was delighted. He touched the stone bench in the garden. It immediately turned into gold. He picked up a pebble from the ground, and found that he held a nugget of gold.

'Wonderful! I shall have a golden palace! I will have a forest of golden trees! Everything around me will be made of gold!' Midas said.

He went round his palace and his garden, turning stone and wood and marble into gold. The roses now had heavy golden blossom and leaves, on golden stems stiff with thorns.

Presently Midas was hungry and thirsty. He went into his palace and sat at his table. He called to his servants to bring him a cup of wine. He was delighted when he saw that as his fingers touched the cup, it turned into a golden goblet.

But as his tongue tasted the wine, that, too, turned into solid gold.

'Bring me food!' he commanded.

His cooks brought their choicest dishes and set them before him. But when the meat and the bread reached his mouth, they became gold, as hard as stone. He took a peach from the golden salver, and it lay heavy and cold in his hand.

'Alas! I have been a fool! I have asked for the Golden Touch, and now, even though I am the richest man in the world, I must die of hunger and thirst!' said Midas.

He called out to the god, Dionysus. He said, 'Great god! You were right and I was wrong. Forgive me! Take back your gift!'

Dionysus laughed. But he was sorry for King Midas. He told him, 'Go and wash in the river and you will be free from the Golden Touch. Then everything that has changed will become itself again.'

The trees swayed in the wind. The flowers smelled sweet. Midas ate a huge meal. He enjoyed the red wine and the good bread.

He was very happy now, even though he was no longer the richest man in the world.

Retold by Catherine Storr

# EXTENSION STUDIES

# A Mesopotamian household, 2000 BC

Mesopotamia, now modern day Iraq, was a centre of trade and home to a civilisation which developed the wheel, writing and farming. Here is a typical family's day.

**4.30am** All slaves rise, dress, pour out water for washing themselves and prepare jugs of water for use by the family.

**5am** The family rise; they wash in water brought by slaves, dress, go to chapel for morning offerings to the dead and prayers to their personal gods. Water is poured into the ground in front of the altar on which incense is burned. In the meantime, the slaves are preparing the breakfast.

**6am** A breakfast of dates and yesterday's bread is served with weak beer. The slaves clear up and make a packed lunch of two pieces of bread ready for the son.

**6.30am** The son leaves for school with his clay tablet of work from the day before. The daughter joins her mother and the slave woman to work in the weaving room. They spin, weave and embroider. The father and slave man go to work in the market place.

**7am – 11am** At school the boys bow to the schoolmaster and then recite their old tablets. They are given new, damp tablets with a text on one side which they must copy on to the reverse. They are then asked to recite from memory (tables, proverbs, lists of places or the part of the Gilgamesh story in which the gods destroy the world by flood).

A home the slave girl starts a fire in the bread oven. She grinds wheat into flour for two hours. Then she rakes the embers out of the hot oven and slaps rounds of bread dough (rising since the day before) inside the oven. While they bake she kneads the new flour into dough to be used the next day. She then prepares a lunch of bread, onions and beer which she takes into the reception room for the daughter and mother. She returns with the slave woman to eat in the kitchen.

In the market square the father works at his craft (seal cutter, blacksmith or potter) while the slave assists or sells from the stalls.

**11am** Everyone eats.

**11.30 am – 2.30 pm** In school the boys shape new clay tablets and copy homework on to them. They then learn by rote a new table or text. The slave girl fetches water from the river to fill the many water jars in the courtyard and kitchen. The slave woman takes the family wash to the river and scrubs it. The mother and daughter go to the market to buy food.

**2.30pm** The son leaves school and lingers in the market to listen to the story-teller on the way home.

**4pm** Everyone arrives home. The son recites both from his new tablets and from memory to his father. Mother and daughter wash and change for dinner.

While the family rests the slaves clean the house, prepare and lay out dinner.

**6pm – 7pm** The family gathers in the reception room for dinner which is served by the slaves. They eat fish (flavoured with cumin and coriander), yoghurt, bread, lettuce, cucumber, dates, apples, figs, pomegranates and pistachios. They drink beer.

The slaves stand behind the family members ready to take food away or bring more. Then they bring a large jar of beer with two straws.

**7pm – 8pm** The parents sit on stools and sip beer from the jar while the children tell other parts of the Gilgamesh story or play tunes on a reed pipe (recorder).

**8pm** The slaves clear away the dinner things, eat their own dinner of bread, onions and yoghurt and tidy the kitchen.

**9pm** The son and daughter go to bed while the slaves continue to work and the parents talk.

**10pm** The parents go to bed and, finally, the slaves are able to lie down to rest in the kitchen.

Harriet Martin

# The treasure of the tomb (Howard Carter and Tutankhamun's treasure)

Howard Carter's hands were trembling. He made a tiny hole in the top left hand corner of the doorway. Then, he tested the air to make sure there were no foul gases.

There were none, so he made the hole larger. He pushed a candle through and peered inside the tomb. At first, he could see nothing. The hot air escaping from the chamber made the candle flicker.

### The glint of gold

As his eyes grew used to the light, he gasped with astonishment at what he saw. The room was full of statues and other objects. Everywhere he looked, there was the glint of gold. He was so amazed that he did not speak.

'Can you see anything?' asked Lord Carnarvon, who was standing behind him.

'Yes,' Carter replied. 'Wonderful things.'

### The tombs of the pharaohs

It was 24 November 1922. For five years, Howard Carter and Lord Carnarvon had been working together. They were both archaeologists – men who study the past by digging up and exploring ruins. They had been searching for the tomb of one of the kings of ancient Egypt.

The people of ancient Egypt believed that there is a life after death. Their kings were known as pharaohs. When a pharaoh died, his body was carefully wrapped up so that it would not decay. A body that is treated in this way is known as a mummy.

### A golden coffin

The body of the pharaoh was put in a golden coffin. This coffin was placed inside several larger coffins, all of which were decorated with jewels. The coffins were then laid in the burial chamber inside the pharaoh's tomb.

### The Valley of the Kings

The tombs of the pharaohs were in a lonely valley known as the Valley of the Kings. The pharaohs were buried in rooms hollowed out deep inside the mountain. Sometimes, the tombs were hundreds of feet deep.

After the burial, the entrance to the tomb was sealed. The tomb was heavily guarded. For, in addition to the burial chamber, there were several other rooms. These rooms were full of rich furniture, clothes and weapons.

## Priceless treasures

There were ornaments and jewels. There was food and wine. There were even royal chariots. The Egyptians believed that the dead king had to take with him all the things he would need in the after life.

Each tomb was full of priceless treasures. There were many attempts to rob the tombs. There were harsh punishments for anyone who was caught. But many robbers thought it was worth the risk.

## Ransacked

When the tombs were opened in the nineteenth century, it was found that most of them had been ransacked. The footprints of the tomb robbers could still be seen in the dust. Sometimes, the mummy had been bundled out of the coffin and the bandages had been ripped off.

By 1914 the Valley of the Kings had been thoroughly explored. The tombs of the pharaohs had been opened, and what was left in them had been taken away. But no one had yet found the tomb of the boy-king Tutankhamun.

Tutankhamun was not an important king. He became the pharaoh at the age of 10 and died before he was 20. Many experts believed that if his tomb was in the Valley of the Kings, it would already have been found.

## The search

Howard Carter did not agree with them. There were several places in the valley where he thought a tomb might be. Carter showed Lord Carnarvon a map of the valley. He explained where he wanted to search. It would cost a lot of money. But Lord Carnarvon was a rich man. He agreed to help Carter and to pay all the expenses of the search.

For five years, Carter searched. He could only work between the autumn and the spring. It was too hot to dig during the summer. His men shifted hundreds of tonnes of rubble and sand. But he did not find a tomb.

## A flight of steps

In the summer of 1922, Lord Carnarvon decided to give up. There seemed to be no point in spending any more money. Carter went to see him. The year before, Carter had found a shallow pit containing some seals with Tutankhamun's name on them. There was a place nearby, which they had not explored yet. He persuaded Lord Carnarvon to pay for him to dig there. If the tomb was not there, he would give up.

On 1 November, Carter and his men started digging.

Four days later, they were clearing away the remains of some ancient workmen's huts, when they uncovered a step cut into the rock. Full of excitement, they went on digging. There was a flight of sixteen steps. The steps led down to a doorway, which was blocked.

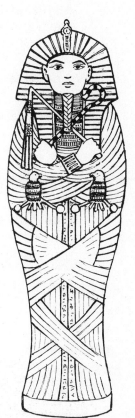

### The doorway

Carter stood before the doorway. Was this the tomb he had been looking for? When they cleared the doorway, would there be anything there?

He desperately wanted to find out, but he knew he would have to wait. He covered the steps up again and left some men on guard. Then, he sent a telegram to Lord Carnarvon in England, telling him of the discovery.

As soon as he heard the news, Lord Carnarvon travelled to Egypt. On 24 November, Carter again stood before the doorway. He was very excited, because they had found some seals on the doorway with Tutankhamun's name on them. But he was also worried. There were signs that the tomb had been broken into twice. Perhaps everything had been stolen.

### An incredible sight

When Carter looked through the hole in the doorway, his worries disappeared. The room was full of riches. He knew at once that they had discovered one of the world's greatest treasures.

Very carefully, Carter set about clearing the blocked doorway. When it was clear, they saw an incredible sight. The room was full of all sorts of objects – bows and arrows, chariots, chests and vases, chairs and stools. Many of them were covered with gold. The men gazed in wonder. One of them said it was like 'an impossible scene from a fairy tale'.

### Two guards

At one end of the room, which became known as the antechamber, stood two life-size figures. They were black and gold, and were made of wood. They were standing on either side of another blocked doorway, guarding it.

Carter knew that beyond this doorway would be the burial chamber. But first he would have to clear the objects from the antechamber. It took him seven weeks.

### A golden throne

There were over six hundred objects. Among them were three splendid wooden couches, covered in gold plate. There was also a magnificent golden throne.

The objects lay scattered about the tomb. Someone must have disturbed the robbers, or caught them in the act. Very few things seemed to be missing. Carter and his team made a careful note of exactly where each object was lying. The objects had been in the tomb for about 3300 years. Many of them had to be handled with great care to make sure they did not fall apart.

## The burial chamber

At last, the work was finished. Carter was ready to open the blocked doorway leading to the burial chamber. On 17 February 1923, a group of about 20 people crowded into the antechamber to watch the opening.

## A solid wall of gold

Working slowly and carefully, Carter made a hole large enough for a torch. When he switched the torch on, he saw what appeared to be a solid wall of gold. As the hole grew larger, the people watching could see that it was one side of a huge, golden tomb. The tomb almost filled the whole burial chamber. It was 17 feet long and 11 feet wide.

When Carter unbolted the doors of the tomb, or shrine, they could see that inside it was another smaller shrine. In fact, there were four shrines. In the centre of the smallest one lay the coffins and the mummy.

Before he could open the coffins, Carter had to take apart the shrines. This took him nearly a year. By the time he was ready to open the coffins, Lord Carnarvon was dead.

## The pharaoh's curse

There is a legend which says that anyone who disturbs the tomb of a pharaoh will die. When Lord Carnarvon died on 5 April 1923, less than 6 months after the tomb was opened, some people said that it was because of the pharaoh's curse. A story went round that he had pricked his finger on an object, which had been deliberately put in the tomb by the priests. In fact, he had been bitten by an insect. The bite became infected, he caught a fever and died.

## The mummy

Because of a quarrel with the Egyptian government it was November 1924 before Howard Carter started work on the coffins. It was not until two years after the discovery of the tomb that he finally looked at Tutankhamun's mummy in its solid gold coffin. Today, the coffin and all the other treasures are in the Egyptian Museum in Cairo. For the treasure which Howard Carter found did not belong to him, but to the Egyptian government.

*From Treasure by John L. Foster*

# The Celts

The Celts were a tall, strong, fair-skinned people. They were very proud of their appearance, and made beautifully polished bronze mirrors in which to admire themselves. Celtic women wore their hair long, either loose or plaited. Celtic men often treated their hair with chalk to make it appear lighter and spiky. Most men shaved, but let their moustaches grow so long that it was difficult to eat or drink.

The Celts often used paints to decorate themselves. Warriors painted their bodies with woad, a blue dye, to make themselves look even more fearsome. Celtic women wore make-up made from berries and herbs to colour their cheeks and eyebrows. They also stained their fingernails with dye from vegetables.

Celtic clothes were brightly coloured. The men wore tight trousers and tunics, the women wore loose woollen dresses and the children wore simple tunics. Both men and women wore cloaks – a thick weave in winter and a thin weave in summer.

Everyone in Celtic Britain belonged to a tribe. Tribes were made up of many families, living as a community. There were over thirty tribes in Celtic Britain, each one ruled by its own king.

The king had a group of advisers to help him rule his tribe and protect it from attack from other tribes. The king's advisers were important noblemen and learned priests called druids. The druids were in charge of all Celtic religious ceremonies. They were experts at looking into the future. They advised the king on what the gods might be trying to tell him.

Below the druids in society came the warriors and their charioteers (chariot drivers). Warriors were important in Celtic society for they defended the tribe and stood for strength, heroism and valour – qualities which the Celts found important. Next, came poets and musicians. The musicians sang songs and recited exciting stories to entertain the king and his advisers. Skilled craftsmen and land-owning farmers were next in importance.

Ordinary people in Celtic society were mostly simple craftsmen, or poor farm workers and servants. A craftsman, such as a blacksmith, would work at one of the furnaces in the hill-fort, making tools like sickles and knives and doing everyday repairs. Most Celtic families led a simple life with few luxuries and little excitement, but they lived in relative safety, the safety of a hill-fort. [This was a] fortified enclosure(s) built on the top of a hill with a good view of the surrounding countryside. In the large hill-forts, there was room for a whole tribe – the king, nobles, warriors, craftsmen, farmers and all their families. Farm animals, such as cattle, were also kept inside the hill-fort in times of danger, but they were mostly left to graze in the surrounding fields.

An army trying to attack the hill-fort would be trapped in the ditch while soldiers defending it could shoot arrows and hurl stones from behind the palisade. The simplest hill-forts had just one ditch and bank. Others had three or even four, one inside the other for extra safety.

The simplest entrances to hill-forts were wooden gates, built across the opening in the bank. Others had more complicated entrances, built almost like a maze. A system of narrow passages, with steep earth banks on each side, helped to confuse and trap the enemy.

Hill-fort life was always busy. Women threshed grain , ground flour on querns or wove cloth on upright looms. Children often helped the women with their weaving. Potters produced many bowls and jars to replace those that got broken. Blacksmiths worked at their furnaces, making farm tools or repairing harnesses. They also taught their sons the trade for the future.

In the countryside around the hill-forts, the Celts grew crops and raised animals. The open landscape was dotted with hamlets, farmsteads and patches of small, squarish fields. These fields, now called Celtic fields, were marked out by low, untidy walls made from stones that ploughmen threw aside as they tended the fields. Ploughing was done with a simple wooden plough, called an ard, pulled along by a pair of oxen.

The Celts grew turnips, cabbages, beans and parsnips. Their main crops were wheat and barley, which were stored for winter. The grain was harvested with small iron or bronze sickles and stored in large jars, or in pits. Flour from the ground grain could be made into porridge, or added to soups to make them thicker. Loaves of bread were baked on hot stones near the fire.

Celtic farmers kept pigs, cattle, sheep and goats. These animals provided fresh meat, as well as milk for making cheese. The Celts also enjoyed hunting wild animals like deer and boar.

For a typical Celtic meal, meat was roasted over the fire on an iron spit or wrapped in straw and baked in the hot embers. Stews were also made and left to bubble slowly in an iron cauldron. Meat that was not needed at once was salted, or hung up in the roof of the hut where it was quickly smoked by the fire. It was important to keep smoked and salted meats for the long, hungry winter months.

From How They Lived: A Celtic Family by Lucilla Watson

# Columbus

Columbus from his after-
deck watched stars, absorbed in water,
melt in liquid amber drifting

through my summer air.
Now with morning, shadows lifting,
beaches stretched before him cold and clear.

Birds circled flapping flag and mizzen
mast: birds harshly hawking, without fear.
Discovery he sailed for was so near.

Columbus from his after-
deck watched heights he hoped for,
rocks he dreamed, rise solid from my simple water.

Parrots screamed. Soon he would touch
our land, his charted mind's desire.
The blue sky blessed the morning with its fire.

But did his vision
fashion, as he watched the shore,
the slaughter that his soldiers

furthered here? Pike
point and musket butt,
hot splintered courage, bones

cracked with bullet shot,
tipped black boot in my belly; the
whip's uncurled desire?

Columbus from his after-
deck saw bearded fig trees, yellow pouis
blazed like pollen and thin

waterfalls suspended in the green
as his eyes climbed towards the highest ridges
where our farms were hidden.

Now he was sure
he heard soft voices mocking in the leaves.
What did this journey mean, this
new world mean: discovery?
Or a return to terrors
he had sailed from, known before?

I watched him pause.

Then he was splashing silence.
Crabs snapped their claws
and scattered as he walked towards our shore.

Edward Kamau Brathwaite

# Around the world with Ferdinand Magellan

Magellan was the son of a Portuguese nobleman. He was born in 1480 and grew up at a time when everyone was talking about exploration. Portuguese sailors were voyaging further and further to the west in search of a route to the Far East.

Magellan first went to sea when he was twenty-five years old, and was badly wounded in a battle with Arabs, off the coast of East Africa. He was made an officer in 1509 following a courageous rescue of his shipmates after they had been lured into a trap by the Sultan of Molucca. A few years later he was accused of dishonest trading, fell out of favour with King Manuel and was unable to gain command of a ship. During this time he heard talk of the discovery of a new ocean (the Pacific) which had been glimpsed by a Spaniard from a hill in Central America.

In 1517 Magellan was invited across the border to Spain and asked to command an expedition for King Charles I. His aim was to find and navigate a westward route to the Spice Islands of the Far East and then to the Philippines where he would claim them for Spain.

It took Magellan 18 months to repair and equip the five ships provided for him by King Charles – his flagship *Trinidad*, the *San Antonio*, the *Concepcion*, the *Victoria* and the *Santiago*. Finally he set sail in 1519 and to begin with the voyage made good progress. On reaching Brazil, Magellan turned south and followed the South American coastline in search of a safe place to anchor for the winter. Here he would make repairs to the ships and seek out fresh supplies of food and water.

Magellan was distrusted by the Spanish captains who mutinied while the ships were in port. However, the ships were soon back under his control and the mutineers condemned to death, although eventually only one of the ringleaders was executed. Then a further disaster occurred when Magellan sent the *Santiago* on a scouting expedition southwards. A fierce storm blew up and wrecked the ship on rocks, although the crew managed to struggle ashore.

When spring arrived the remaining four ships headed south again until after a number of false alarms Magellan found the narrow channel that would lead him between Tierra del Fuego and the mainland of South America. (Now called the Magellan Strait.) Rough seas and howling winds slowed his progress while the *San Antonio* deserted and returned to Spain. Finally after a month of battling against everything the weather could throw at him, his ships emerged into calm sea. Magellan referred to this as 'the Sea of Peace', the Pacific Ocean.

Magellan headed for the Moluccas, or rather he headed for the position where he thought the Moluccas would be, but mapmakers were unaware of the vast extent of the Pacific Ocean. The first crossing of the Pacific took sixteen weeks, during which time there was no fresh food to be had. The crew were ravaged by scurvy and water was undrinkable. To satisfy their hunger pangs they ate the rats in the bilges along with biscuits that were infested with worms. They even cooked and ate the leather from the rigging. Thankfully the weather was calm as the weak crew would never have copied with a storm.

At last they sighted land, a group of islands called the Marianas. The natives were unfriendly and looted Magellan's ships, taking advantage of the weak state of his crew. Magellan picked forty of his strongest men and attacked the islanders. They burnt their huts and carried back as much fresh food as they could plunder. A week later they reached the Philippines where their welcome was warmer, and where Magellan made trading links and claimed the islands for Spain. For many months the fleet lay at anchor off the island of Cebu where the ruler and his subjects were converted to Christianity.

Magellan then agreed to help the King of Cebu attack nearby Mactan Island whose ruler refused to become a Christian. However Magellan attacked with only a small number of men and they were driven back. Magellan was killed during this retreat while his Spanish captains watched the events and refused to help. As they saw it, Magellan had upset their plans to reach the Spice Islands.

Two ships, the *Trinidad* and the *Victoria*, finally reached their goal on 6 November 1521, more than two years after they had set sail. Here they loaded up with valuable cargoes of cloves, silk and gold. Then when they were about to depart for home, the *Trinidad* sprung a leak. The *Victoria* crossed the Indian Ocean and sailed around the Cape of Good Hope, finally reaching Seville. Its commander, Sebastian de Cano, and just seventeen men had completed the first circumnavigation of the world.

Brian Moses

# The people of Mexico through Spanish eyes

The people of Mexico are well made, tending to be tall rather than short. They have dark, brownish skins and are good looking.
The Men: The men dress in cotton cloaks, like sheets, though not so large, with decorated bands and borders, and they are knotted over the chest. In winter time they cover themselves with cloaks woven of tiny feathers. They cover their private parts with very showy cloths of many colours. They wear sandals with highly decorated heels. They wear their hair long and tied in various ways.
*The Anonymous Conquistador (1556)*

Some pierce their ears and put very large and ugly objects into them; others make holes in their nostrils and lips and put in them large round stones which look like mirrors; while others split their lower lips as far as the gums and hang there some large stones or gold ornaments so heavy that they drag the lips down, making them look ugly.
*Letter from the Town Council of Vera Cruz, 10th July 1519*

The Women: The women wear sleeveless cotton blouses, long and full with decorated borders. They wear two or three of these, one of them longer than the others, to make them look like skirts. From the waist down they wear another kind of dress of pure cotton which reaches the knees. They have very beautiful hair, either black or brown, which they wear long, covering their backs.
*The Anonymous Conquistator (1556)*

From The Conquest of Mexico – Aztec and Spanish Accounts

# The Spaniards through Aztec eyes

When the Spaniards first landed on the coast of Mexico, they were met by officials, sent by Angry Lord, ruler of the Aztec Empire. The Spaniards put on a military display. The officials returned to Cactus Rock to report to Angry Lord. According to one account, this is how the Aztecs described the strangers:

'They dress in metal and wear metal hats on their heads. Their swords are metal. Their bows are metal. Their shields are metal. Their spears are metal.

The strangers' bodies are completely covered, so that only their faces can be seen. Their skin is white as if it were made of lime plaster. They have yellow hair, though some have black. Their beards are long and yellow, and their moustaches are also yellow. Their hair is curly, with very fine strands.
*Sahagun*

Their deer carry them on their backs wherever they wish to go. These deer are as tall as the roof of a house.

Their dogs are very big, with folded ears and long, dangling tongues. Their eyes are burning yellow and flash like fire. They are very powerful. They run here and there panting, and they are flecked like a jaguar.
*Sahagun*

The thunder is deafening. A thing like a ball of stone comes out of its belly. It comes out shooting sparks and raining fire. The smoke smells horrible, like rotten mud. If it is aimed at a mountain, the mountain cracks open. If it is aimed at a tree, it shatters the tree to dust.'
*Sahagun*

From The Conquest of Mexico – Aztec and Spanish Accounts

# In search of a north-west passage: Martin Frobisher

By the 1570s, English hopes for a route to Cathay had switched to the north-west. Sir Humphrey Gilbert wrote a book in which he argued that a north-west passage could be found much further south than the icy north-east route.

Gilbert raised the money to try out his idea. The man he chose to lead his planned voyage of exploration was an ex-pirate called Martin Frobisher.

In June 1576, Frobisher sailed from the Thames with three ships. In fierce weather, one of the ships sank. Off Greenland, the crew of the second ship decided to sail home – they could see that the north-west was just as cold as the north-east.

Frobisher sailed on alone and reached Baffin Island, where he believed he had found the strait leading to Cathay. He called it Frobisher's Strait. In fact, it was only a bay, a dead end, known today as Frobisher Bay. There he saw a strange sight ahead of him. The strange men that Frobisher met called themselves the Inuit, meaning 'people' and they called their leather boats kayaks. Today, they are often known as Eskimos, which means 'eaters of raw meat'. This was what the peoples who lived to the south of the Inuit called them.

The English sailors thought the Inuit were simple savages. Yet they had worked out how to survive in one of the coldest and harshest places on earth. The Inuit lived by hunting and fishing. Animals such as seals supplied all their needs. Skins were used for clothes, for tents and for boats. The Inuit also trained dogs called huskies to pull their sledges when they travelled overland.

Their life was so well suited to the icy climate that it hardly changed over the years. Three hundred years after Frobisher's voyage, the Inuit were still living in very much the same way.

Dionyse Settle, who sailed with Frobisher on his second voyage to Baffin Island, described the Inuit way of life. It seemed very strange to the explorers:

'They eat their meat all raw. For lack of water, they will eat ice, as pleasantly as we will do sugar candy...

'They keep certain dogs not much unlike wolves, which they yoke together, as we do horses, to a sled. And when the dogs are no longer fit for this, they eat them...

'Those beasts, fishes and birds which they kill are their meat, drink, clothing, houses, bedding, shoes, thread and sails for their boats, and almost all their riches.'

Five Englishmen went ashore to trade with the Inuit, and disappeared. Frobisher was desperate to get them back. He decided to capture an Inuit man to swap for them. He drew one to the ship's side by holding out a bell

and ringing it. When a man paddled up in a kayak, Frobisher pulled him on board, still in his boat.

Even though Frobisher had captured the Inuit, he could not get his own men back. They were never seen again.

Frobisher eventually gave up and sailed home, bringing with him the strange man and his boat. The Inuit caused a great stir back in London, though he died soon after from a cold.

Even more sensational was a piece of black rock which Frobisher had found on Baffin Island. Experts in London said that it contained gold. It seemed that the English would not have to find Cathay after all. There was enormous wealth to be had much closer to home.

In 1577, Frobisher sailed back to Baffin Island with three ships. This time, he was after gold. The search for Cathay was almost forgotten.

Frobisher spent a month mining and collected 200 tons of the black rock. He also captured an Inuit man and a woman with a young baby. Then he set sail for England.

Back in England, the Inuit man gave a display of duck hunting in his kayak on the River Avon. He was also introduced to Queen Elizabeth I. She was so impressed by him that she gave him permission to hunt swans on the Thames. After a month in England the Inuit died, just like the first captive.

George Best, Frobisher's second in command, described what happened when the captured Inuit man and woman were brought together for the first time:

'At their first meeting, they looked at each other very sadly for a long time, without saying anything, as if their grief had taken away their power of speech. Then the woman suddenly looked away and began to sing, as if she was thinking of another matter.

'Being brought together again, the man broke the silence first, and with a serious face began to tell a long solemn tale to the woman, who listened closely to him.

'Afterwards, having grown to know each other better, they were left together, so that I think the one would hardly have lived without the comfort of the other.'

In 1578, Frobisher made a third voyage with a great fleet of 15 ships. This was paid for by some of the richest people in England. They had joined a new Company of Cathay, hoping to share in the gold found by Frobisher.

Among the crews were thirty Cornish tin miners, most of them 'pressed', or forced to join the crews against their will. This was a common method of getting people to crew ships in the sixteenth century.

It was a terribly cold summer and Frobisher's Strait was almost blocked by ice. The ships lost sight of each other in thick fog, and one of them sank in a fierce storm.

After reaching Baffin Island, the miners spent a month gathering the black rocks, in conditions of great hardship. When winter came, the ships sailed home carrying over 1,000 tons of rock.

Bad news was waiting for Frobisher in England. The black rocks were not gold at all, but worthless iron pyrites – known as 'fool's gold'. The Company of Cathay lost all its money and Frobisher was in disgrace. The black rocks ended up being used to mend the roads.

From The Search for a Southern Route: Exploration and Encounters (1450–1550) by Peter Chrisp

# Plague at Eyam

### April 8

It was Palm Sunday today and Father and I managed to get to church for the first time since Christmas. The paths were still too slippery for Mother to come now that she is having a baby.

The village was strangely quiet as we walked down the main street. The church yard had so many freshly-dug graves that it looked like a muddy field. I kept very close to Father as we went in.

There were gaps in the church where whole families used to stand. The Sydalls, the Halksworths, the Thorpes, the Coopers, Torres, Ragges, all with just one or two left standing alone with no one daring to go near. All through the service I kept turning round to see which of my friends was there, until Father stopped me.

At the end of the service Mistress Mompesson came to us and asked after Mother. Father told her that all was well. She told us that the Plague had not stopped all through the winter months. Her husband was afraid that now the weather was warmer it would get worse. For once I was glad that we live so far away from the village.

As we started to walk home some of my friends called me to join them. Father snatched me back and held me fast. He told me that I must keep away from the children in the village. I was shocked and argued that they were my friends and they were not sick. He just looked at me and I knew he meant it. He kept hold of my arm as we walked on and I could not bear to look back. I felt so ashamed, as if I had betrayed my friends. I thought that they would never want to play with me again and I cried most of the way home.

**May 15**

Isaac and Father have been keeping a close watch on the sheep and lambs for fear of foxes and dogs. This morning, Isaac showed me how to use a sling to cast stones at them.

Mistress Mompesson came up to talk to Mother today. She was upset because she had just said goodbye to her two children. They had been sent off to Yorkshire to their uncle to keep them safe from the Plague. She cried and cried and said that she was sure she would never see them again. I felt really sorry for her.

**June 8**

The weather is very hot and we have started the shearing with the Mortins. Mother is very big now and she needs me to help her nearly all the time.

Yesterday Father brought in a cradle for the baby which he had been making. It is lovely and it rocks. Mother was really pleased. He put it up in their bed chamber. This baby seems to be taking for ever to come!

The parson and his wife both called after supper. Father went outside for a walk with the parson. While they were gone, Mistress Mompesson told Mother that the village was in a real state of terror because the Plague had started to get much worse. Everyone was talking about running away to escape. She said her husband had met with John Stanley, the old parson, and both have agreed that the best thing to do is to seal off the village to stop the Plague spreading to all the other villages around. They are both going to speak to the parishioners on Sunday after the service.

**June 10**

Father stayed for the meeting after church yesterday but I had to come straight home. When he got back he said nothing so I had to ask Isaac what had happened. He said that the mood was really nasty and if the old parson hadn't been there to shout at the men there would have been a riot. In the end they all agreed to abide by the parson's decision not to let anyone leave or come into the parish. The boundary stones will mark the limit and we are not to go beyond them. I asked if that meant we couldn't take our wool and lambs to Tideswell market and he just nodded. 'But we

will starve,' I said and he explained that the parson had written to the Earl of Devonshire and he would supply us with all we need until the Plague has stopped.

Later on, I heard the two Kempe boys saying that, from now on, no one who has died of the Plague is to be buried in the graveyard. Instead they are to be buried on their own land without a burial service or anything. Father saw that I was listening and silenced the boys.

On the way home I asked Father if it was true that we were not to go over the parish boundary now. He nodded grimly and said that he had sworn an oath that none of his family would try to go out of the parish until the Plague had ended. It made me feel frightened inside, like I was trapped.

*Gill Goddard*

# Women in science

Although many women throughout history have been involved in the development of science, their work has gained little recognition. For a number of reasons their achievements have often been ignored and their names left out of books. Women were unable to attend universities and were excluded from scientific societies and laboratories. Because they had little scientific education, many women could only serve as assistants to male scientists. The situation has improved slowly, but there are still far fewer women working in the sciences than there are men.

### Early women scientists
Although there were women doctors in Ancient Egypt and Greece, there were very few opportunities for women to work in medicine and science in the ancient world. Accounts of the lives of successful women were invariably written by men who dismissed women scientists as immoral and dangerous. The first such scientist whose life is well-documented is Hypatia. Most of her writings have been lost, but there are a number of references to them by other scientists. Hypatia was born in Alexandria in Egypt, where she taught mathematics and philosophy. Her most important work was in algebra and geometry, but she was also interested in mechanics and technology. In addition she designed several scientific instruments, including a plane astrolabe. This was used for measuring the positions of the stars, planets and the sun.

### Abbess and physician
Hildegard of Bingen was the abbess of a convent in Germany. She was educated in a wide range of subjects, including music and medicine. She wrote many books on religion as well as a natural history encyclopaedia called *Liber simplicis medicinae* which described animals and minerals and as many as 230 plants and 60 trees.

Hildegard devised a number of maps of the universe. In her first plan of the universe, the earth lies in the middle surrounded by the stars and planets.

### A forgotten mathematician

Anne, Countess of Conway (1631–79), a mathematician and philosopher, was born in London. Her brother, who acted as her tutor, supplied her with books and introduced her to the ideas of Descartes. Her country house became a well-known meeting place for scholars. Anne Conway's book, *The Principles of the most Ancient and Modern Philosophy*, was published eleven years after her death by a Dutch chemist called Francis van Helmont. It contained many of her scientific ideas and had a great influence on a German mathematician called Gottfried Leibniz (1646–1716). Although Leibniz acknowledged her importance, Conway's work was attributed to van Helmont and her name was soon forgotten.

### A self-taught astronomer

Caroline Herschel (1750–1848) was born into a family of German musicians. In 1772 she moved to England to join her brother William, an astronomer. After teaching herself astronomy and mathematics with his help, she became his assistant. Later, in 1787, she became the first woman to be appointed assistant to the Court Astronomer.

### Finding new comets

Herschel became recognised throughout Europe as a great astronomer. As well as her important collaborations with her brother, independently she discovered many new comets. She won a number of awards for her work, including the Gold Medal of the Royal Astronomical Society in 1828. Her success helped to open up astronomy to other women of her time.

### Spreading scientific ideas

Mary Somerville made important contributions to science education. Born in Scotland, she became known as 'the Queen of the 19th-century science'. Her first scientific paper, *On the Magnetizing Power of the More Refrangible Solar Rays*, had to be submitted to the Royal Society by her husband because women were banned from the organisation. In 1831 she published *Mechanism of the Heavens*. As well as being her interpretation of the work of a French scientist called Pierre de Laplace (1749–1827), the book contained many original ideas of her own. For the rest of the century it was a standard text in the study of advanced mathematics.

### The first computer programmer

Ada, Countess of Lovelace, daughter of the poet Lord Byron, studied astronomy, Latin, music and mathematics. She worked with an English mathematician called Charles Babbage (1792–1871), as the designer of arithmetical operations for his calculating machines. As these machines are now often seen as the forerunners of computers, in a sense Lovelace was the first computer programmer. Her work for the machines and her ideas on their uses were published in 1843. But as it was considered unsuitable at that time for women to publish under their own names, she only signed the work with her initials. As a result, her work as a mathematician, like those of many other women scientists, has been largely forgotten.

FromThe Usborne Book of Scientists: From Archimedes to Einstein by Struan Reid and Patricia Fara

# Index

# Acknowledgements

## The publishers gratefully acknowledge permission to reproduce the following copyright material:

©1994 Moira Andrew for 'August 1939'; BBC Enterprises for 'Who was Odysseus?' from *The World of Odysseus* by Neil Grant (1990, BBC Enterprises) and 'Like foreigners to us' from *Children at War* edited by Patricia Williams (1989, BBC Enterprises); B T Batsford Ltd for 'A Tudor criminal: Ned Browne' from *Tudor People* by John Fines (1977, B T Batsford); Belitha Press Ltd for 'King Midas and his gold' from *King Midas and his Gold* by Catherine Storr (1985, Belitha Press); ©1994 Margaret Blount for 'Setting sail with John Cabot 1497'; ©1994 Ann Bonner for 'Billy the nailer' and 'The seamstress's story'; ©1994 Alan Brown for 'The Coronation'; Cambridge University Press for 'Nadia Cattouse' from *Keep Smiling Through – Women in the Second World War* (1989, CUP), 'The School Year' by Wes Magee from *The Witch's Brew and Other Poems* (1989, CUP), 'Photographs' by Brian Moses from *Hippopotamus Dancing* (1994, CUP) and 'Summer: the cloak of the wind' from *The Vikings: Fact and fiction* by Robin Place (1985, CUP); Casarotto Ramsay Ltd for 'Evacuees' from *Evacuees* by Jack Rosenthal (1978, Penguin Books); ©1994 Doris Corti for 'A kitchen in the early 1930s'; ©1994 John Cotton for 'The wireless set'; ©1994 Jan Dean for 'The corner shop'; Faber & Faber Ltd for 'Twopence a tub' by Susan Price from *Middle English Anthology* (1985, Faber & Faber); ©1994 John Foster for 'Grandad's clothes', 'Grandma's doll', 'Viking gods' and 'Viking longhouses' from 'Viking stories'; ©1994 Gill Goddard for 'Plague at Eyam' and 'Will Martin's diary'; ©1994 Marlene Greenslate for 'The day the Queen came to stay'; ©1994 Peter Hanratty for 'Teds' and 'The taking of Silchester'; ©1994 Trevor Harvey for 'The King is dead'; Hodder & Stoughton Ltd for 'Looking Back' from *A Century of Change: 20th Century Homes* by John Foster (1990, Hodder & Stoughton) and 'The treasure of the tomb (Howard Carter and Tutankhamun's treasure)' from *Treasure* by John L. Foster (1980, Edward Arnold); ©1994 James Kirkup for 'The children of change'; Larousse plc for 'The aftermath of the Armada – a famous escape' from *The National Trust Book of the Armada* by Mary Connatty (1987, Kingfisher Books); ©1994 Karlen Lawrence for 'Did you know?'; London Borough of Richmond upon Thames and Valerie Boyes, History Advisory Services for 'Grandad's Washday' from *In Living Memory* and 'Spaceman James' by Marjorie Williams (1991, Education in Richmond); Longman Group UK for 'Florence Nightingale and Mary Seacole' from *Lights and Candles Key Stage 1 (A Sense of History Series)* and 'The Olympic Games' from *Birthdays Key Stage 1 (A Sense of History Series)* by Sallie Purkis (1991, Longman Group); ©1994 John Lynch for 'Lindisfarne AD 783'; ©1994 Wes Magee for 'The chimney boy's song'; ©1993 Harriet Martin 'A Mesopotamian household, 2000 BC' from 'Family Life' in *Junior Focus No 62* (1993, Scholastic); Sarah Matthews, Literary executrix and joint copyright holder for 'The hill fort' ©1991 Stanley Cook; ©1994 Robin Mellor for 'Theseus and the Minotaur'; ©1994 Pratima Mitchell for 'Home from the sea'; ©1994 Tony Mitton for 'Child', 'Honey (Anglo-Saxon monologue)', 'Shopping lists', 'The magical machine', and 'The train to work'; ©1994 Brian Moses for 'Around the world with Ferdinand Magellan', 'Be there or be square', 'Having a lovely time: bathing and bathing machines', 'Interview: Mrs Ivy Green, Ramsgate' and 'Letter from a Roman soldier'; Thomas Nelson & Sons Ltd for 'Bath night' from *London Morning* by Valerie Avery (1969, Arnold Wheaton) and 'The story of Daedalus and Icarus' from *Myths and Legends Book 1: Classical and northern stories* by David Oakden (1979, Arnold Wheaton); Oxford University Press for '2. Columbus' from 'The Emigrants' by Edward Kamau Brathwaite in *Every Poem Tells a Story* (1988, OUP), 'Enkales: my life as a slave' and 'Timon goes to school' from *The Greeks* by Roy Burrell (1990, OUP), 'A whirlpool and a monster' and 'The wooden horse' from *The Legend of Odysseus* by Peter Connolly (1989, OUP), 'Beowulf fights with Grendel' from *Beowulf* edited by Kevin Crossley-Holland (1982, OUP), 'The journey I will never forget' by Tran Dang (aided by Mrs Averil Weekes) from *My Grandmother's Motorbike: Story writing in Primary Schools* (1991, OUP), 'Thomas' by Michael Harrison from *Junk Mail* (1993, OUP), 'No dogs, children or coloureds' from *Milk and Honey* by Avril Rowlands (1989, OUP) and 'Harvest home', 'Meals and manners' and 'School' from *Lark Rise to Candleford* by Flora Thompson (1945, OUP); Pan Macmillan for 'Apples of the Gods' from *The Exploits of Hercules* by Douglas Hill (1979, Piccolo) and 'The Warrior Queen' from *The Warrior Queen* by

Martin Mellett (1978, Piccolo); ©1994 Bette Paul for 'Lessons in the air-raid shelter'; Pavilion Books Ltd for 'Village shop' from *War Boy: A country childhood* by Michael Foreman (1989, Pavilion); Penguin Books Ltd for 'Mum, Dad and Me' by James Berry from *When I Dance* (1990, Hamish Hamilton), 'Watching the Armada sail past' from *When the Beacons Blazed* by Hestor Burton (1978, Hamish Hamilton), 'Peter and Kate on the move' from *High Days and Holidays* by Eileen Colwell (1989, Puffin), 'The workhouse' from *Street Child* by Berlie Doherty (1989, Hamish Hamilton), 'First invasion of Britain by Julius Caesar (55BC)' from *The Conquest of Gaul* translated by S. A. Handford and revised by Jane F. Gardner (1982, Penguin Classics) Text ©1951 The Estate of S. A. Handford and ©1982 Jane F. Gardner, '...the terrible laws the English government has made against us...' from *A Pistol at Greenyards* by Mollie Hunter (1965, Hamish Hamilton), 'Doctor Kelly's cures' from *The Weather Witch* by Paul Stewart (1989, Viking Children's Books); ©1992 David Poulter for 'Odin's men'; Random House UK Ltd for 'The girl becomes a mother' from *I was there: Ancient Greece* by John D. Clare (1993, Bodley Head) and 'My Mammy sen' for me' from *Mammy, Sugar Falling Down* by Trish Cooke (1989, Hutchinson); Reed Consumer Books Ltd for 'Treats' from *A Strong and Willing Girl* by Dorothy Edwards (1980, Methuen), 'The pawnbroker's apprentice' from *Apprentices* by Leon Garfield (1984, William Heinemann Ltd), 'Air raid on Guernsey' from *Tomorrow is a Stranger* by Geoffrey Trease (1987, Heinemann) and 'Sea battle' from *Crossing to Salamis* by Jill Paton Walsh (1977, William Heinemann Ltd); Rogers, Coleridge & White for 'The castle' by Tony Bradman from *Castles Poems* (1993, OUP) and 'from "Autobiography"' from *Collected Poems 1967–85* by Adrian Henri (1986, Allison & Busby); Severn House Publishers Ltd for 'High seas adventures' from *The Spanish Boy* by Juliet Dymoke (1987, Severn House); Simon & Schuster Education for 'A new boy in town' and 'Fun and games' from *Living in the Past: Britons and Romans* by Haydn Middleton (1983, Basil Blackwell) and 'Alfred the hero' from *Living in the Past: The Dark Ages* by Haydn Middleton (1984, Basil Blackwell); Simon & Schuster Young Books for 'The boar hunt' from *Everyday Life of a Celtic Farmer* by Giovanni Caselli (1985, MacDonald); ©1993 Anna Simon for 'Marcus and the Hare' from *Scholastic Collections: Drama and Short Plays* (1993, Scholastic); ©1986 Eric Slayter for 'Changing Times' from *Marbles in My Pocket* (1986, Macmillan Educational); Avis Thornton for 'Illness in the family' from *Pettie – Memories of a Victorian Nursery* by Annie Beatrice Champion (1989, Cicerone Press); Tressell Publications for 'The people of Mexico through Spanish eyes' and 'The Spaniards through Aztec eyes' from *The Conquest of Mexico: Aztec and Spanish accounts* by Peter Chrisp and David Simkin (1991, Tressell Publications); Two-Can Publishing Ltd for 'Thor visits the land of the giants' from *The Vikings* by Robert Nicholson and Claire Watts (1991, Two-Can Publishing); Usborne Publications for 'Women in science' from *The Usborne Book of Scientists: From Archimedes to Einstein* by Struan Reid and Patricia Fara; Walker Books Ltd for 'Mr Mandolini and his dancing bear' and 'The blacksmith' from *Our Village* Text ©1988 John Yeoman (1988, Walker Books); Watts Publishing Group for '1950s schooldays' from *When I Was Young: The Fifties* by Neil Thomson and Pat Scott (1991, Franklin Watts), 'Starting work' from *When I Was Young: The Thirties* by Neil Thomson and Glynn Davies (1991, Franklin Watts) and 'Me and my family' from *When I was Young (Early 20th Century)* by Ruth Thomson (1989, Franklin Watts); Wayland Publishers Ltd for 'In search of a north-west passage: Martin Frobisher' from *The Search for a Southern Route: Exploration and Encounters (1450–1550)* by Peter Chrisp (1993, Wayland) and 'The Celts' from *A Celtic Family (How They Lived series)* by Lucilla Watson (1987, Wayland); ©1988 Barry Wheeler for 'A Victorian schoolmaster' from *The Journal of a Victorian Schoolmaster in Dorset 1863–64* edited and compiled by Barry Wheeler (1988, Winterbourne Press); Young Library Ltd for 'The two Annas' from *Anna Then and Anna Now* by Josette Blanco and Claude d' Ham (1988, Young Library).

Every effort has been made to trace copyright holders for material in this anthology and the publishers apologise for any inadvertent omissions.